GARLIC
&
ONIONS

The Many Uses & Medicinal Benefits

GARLIC
&
ONIONS

The Many Uses &
Medicinal Benefits

Margaret Briggs

Abbeydale Press

ISBN 978-1-86147-233-5

1 3 5 7 9 10 8 6 4 2

Published by Abbeydale Press
an imprint of Bookmart Ltd
Registered number 2372865
Trading as Bookmart Ltd
Blaby Road, Wigston, Leicester
LE18 4SE, England

Produced for Bookmart Limited
Design and cover by Omnipress Ltd
Illustrations by Tegan Sharrard

Printed in Dubai

ABOUT THE AUTHOR

Margaret Briggs was a teacher for 30 years, working in Kent, Germany, North Yorkshire and Sussex.

Since leaving teaching she has had more time for gardening and cooking and has embarked on a second career as a freelance writer, researcher and editor, alongside her writer husband, Lol. Six years ago the couple bought a dilapidated house in south-west France. The house is now restored and Margaret and Lol divide their time between Sussex and the Gironde, with two contrasting gardens to develop.

Margaret has written seven other books in this series including: *Vinegar — 1001 Practical Uses*, *Gardening Hints and Tips*, *Porridge Oats — and their Many Uses* and *Honey — and its many health benefits*.

CONTENTS

The Venerable Globe and the Stinking Rose

Think of an onion: a medium-sized globe, with a brownish
-bronze exterior that feels smooth and comforting in the
hand. The outer skin has a sheen about it that exudes
well-being and homeliness. Cut off the base and the top
and there is a faint hint of food to come. The smell can
even make you feel hungry. Now take off the outer layers
(not too many, mind) and look at the white, glossy
sphere. The aroma may be getting stronger and you may
see the slightest trace of milky liquid escaping between
the layers at the top or base. Now slice the onion to
reveal the layers inside. It brings tears to the eyes to see
the beauty within. I'll stop before I get too emotional.

It is no surprise that the Ancient Egyptians worshipped
the onion. The concentric rings encompass the earth,
life, everything they held dear. As well as that, onions
provided a source of health, wealth and happiness. The
onion is the only vegetable to have been cast in gold by
the Egyptians and they used the beneficial chemicals
from onions and other alliums like garlic to treat
illnesses, counter infection and to bury with their dead.

Garlic has so many compounds of benefit to our bodies
packed inside each little clove that I can't imagine how
anyone gets through life without it. Admittedly, the odour
of stale garlic is something to be avoided, but this seems
a small price to pay for the benefits and preventions for
so many ailments. I think whoever coined the name
'Stinking Rose' has missed something.

Throughout history onions and garlic have been fairly high
profile and are now grown all over the world in at least
175 countries. They have inspired writers and thinkers,
been associated with the supernatural and many legends.
Even architects of Orthodox churches have been inspired
by them.

Now, back to that onion. What will it be today? Onion rings, caramelised with pork chops, or a curry with plenty of garlic, ginger and spices? I'll just get a tissue and have a good cry while I decide.

Know Your Onions

Imagine food without onions! The family of plants that all types of onions, shallots and garlic belong to is called *Allium*, which in turn is part of a bigger family called *Liliales*. This order of flowering plants is known as monocotyledon, which means that they have a single seed leaf. Lilies are the most well-known family of this group, but onions also belong, as well as asparagus, yams, amaryllis, hyacinth, tulips, lily of the valley and narcissus. There's a clue to this relationship if you look at the flowers of amaryllis and onions or garlic bulbs that have gone to seed. The flowers are stunning.

WHAT'S IN A NAME?
Alliaceae is the group name for the allium family and relatives, of which there are about 670 species. About a quarter of the species is cultivated.

The genus name, *Allium*, is said to come from the Celtic *all*, meaning pungent. The species name, *cepa*, is from the Latin for onion.

The word onion comes from the Latin word *unio*, meaning a large pearl. Other sources suggest that *unio* means one, signifying that the bulb is of one unit. It is easy to see how these comparisons came about. The word became corrupted to *unyon* during the Middle Ages.

ALLIUM CEPA
This is the common garden onion and is a native of western Asia. It probably originates from between Turkmenistan and Afghanistan, where some of its relatives still grow in the wild. Various related varieties are grown because of suitability for drying or for producing what are called spring onions, scallions or green onions. Shallots also belong to this group. Four main groups are grown here in Britain, i.e. a main crop grown for harvesting in the autumn, sown in the spring; a summer crop grown from autumn planting or from sets in spring; salad onions, harvested young and green, which do not store; pickling onions, sown in spring and maturing quickly in the summer months.

Onions are herbaceous, biennial plants with edible bulbs.

They commonly have one or more leafless stalks and can reach heights of up to nearly 2 metres (6 feet). Onion eaters aren't normally aware of the beautiful flowers produced by some varieties, as they detract from the development of the edible bulb at the base of the plant. Onions can be grown from seed, normally small and black, or from small bulbs or sets which are transplanted once germinated and established.

Onions vary a great deal in size, colour and strength of flavour. Those produced in warmer climates tend to be milder and sweeter than those from cooler climates. They have a more limited growing season and don't store so well. Common colours for onions are yellow, red and white. Large, globe shaped onions are usually grown for storage and after harvesting they are dried out for a time to promote the development of crisp, dry skins which help to keep the insides fresh.

You can find a list of different varieties later in the book.

ALLIUM ASCALONICUM (SHALLOTS)
These are bulbs about 2 centimetres (1 inch) across which form clusters. They are ideal for pickling and are often used as a substitute for common onions. They like open, sunny sites and fertile, well drained soil that has previously been improved for other crops.

The shallot or eschallot is supposedly named after its place of origin in Ascalon, Syria.

In some parts of the world shallots replace onions because the temperature is too high for seed production, and the climate too humid. The shorter cycle of shallots (60–75 days) can give two crops a year, especially along the Gulf of Guinea. Yellow or red/purple shallots are grown in many other parts of Africa, including Côte d'Ivoire, Ghana, Benin, Ethiopia and Tanzania. The spicy taste and high dry matter content (15–18%) of shallots have made them attractive for growers further from the equator.

Shallots are grown by planting a single bulb, around

which many more bulbs will form. There is much confusion over the term scallion, which sometimes refers to the shallot and later refers to the Welsh Onion.

ALLIUM SATIVUM

This is the Latin name for garlic. It is believed to have originated in Kazakhstan, Uzbekistan and western China. Garlic now grows wild in Italy and southern France. It has been used throughout recorded history for both cooking and medicinal purposes. It has a characteristic pungent flavour that mellows and sweetens considerably with cooking. The bulb is called a head of garlic and is made up of a number of cloves. There may be as many as 20 cloves to one head. The grey-green leaves and stems are sometimes eaten and, left to mature, the plant will produce small, white flowers in summer. Flower heads need to be removed, to help the bulbs develop. Varieties include purple and white colouring and elephant garlic, with a less strong flavour and giant bulbs. After onion, garlic is the second most widely used cultivated *Allium*.

Garlic can be propagated from planting a single clove, rather like the method of growing shallots. Although a perennial plant, it is usually treated as an annual. Each clove contains about 0.1% essential oil and is known to have antiseptic and disinfectant properties. The wild garlic — or crow garlic — found in many countries, including Britain and the USA, are commonly called weeds, and although they smell strongly they don't have the same flavour.

ALLIUM PORRUM

Allium porrum is the Latin name for leeks. Leeks are hardy, biennial plants which can grow vigorously. They can be grown as an annual for use during the autumn and winter months. They have a milder flavour than onions and are much used in European cooking in soups, stews and casseroles. In the first season long thin leaves grow from a compressed stem. They look just like spring onions in their early stages. The actual bulb is cylindrical and full of concentric layers. It is as large at the base as at the top. Stems have a mild onion flavour and often need blanching. The layers have a tendency to collect soil and particles of dirt within, so careful cleaning is advised. The seeds produced are small, black and angular, with irregular shapes. Leeks are native to the Middle East and to the eastern Mediterranean. In Britain they have traditionally been grown for show in the north of the country. The leek is also the national emblem of Wales.

ALLIUM SCHOENPRASUM

Allium schoenprasum is the Latin name given to chives. This small, hardy perennial plant is grown as a herb. Small, white, elongated bulbs grow with leaves which are tubular. The flowers create impressive displays of blue to rose-pink spheres rising above the foliage. They are often grown in pots in sunny sites for ease of harvesting. Propagation is normally achieved by dividing clumps, although seeds can be set. The leaves are used for flavouring salads, soups, egg dishes and sauces. Chives thrive in loamy soils and sunny or semi-shaded locations and are particularly suited to pots and window boxes.

ORNAMENTAL ONIONS

Species such as *Allium moly* are grown as ornamentals. This is a fairly low-growing yellow variety. Others, such as *Allium giganteum*, as the name suggests, reach well over a metre (or up to 4 feet) in height. You can find a list of ornamental allium varieties at the end of the book.

A History of
Allium Eaters

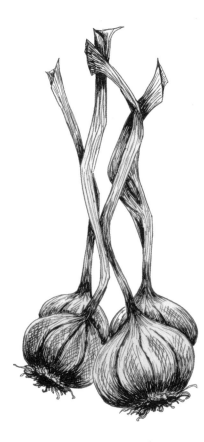

Nobody is quite sure when the first onions were cultivated, but we do know that wild onions have been around for thousands of years. Excavations at Bronze Age archaeological sites dating from 5000 BC have apparently discovered that onions were eaten alongside figs and dates, although there wouldn't have been much left of the onions because they are soft, watery and without stone or pip. It is more than likely that prehistoric people ate onions and even stored them for use during the winter months, because onions can be dried to preserve them and don't need to be salted or preserved in any other form to prevent them perishing. Since onions grow in a wide variety of regions throughout the world they were probably eaten in many cultures before they were cultivated, or before farming was established. Some historians believe that onions were first cultivated in Central Asia, although others suggest Iran or Pakistan as the most likely sites.

We need to leap forward a couple of thousand years to the times of the Ancient Egyptians to have stronger evidence of their role in rituals and worship, as well as their consumption by at least some groups of Egyptians. Leeks and garlic were probably cultivated at about the same time.

Onions weren't just food to the Egyptians: they were worshipped by them for their spherical shape and concentric rings which came to symbolise eternal life. Onions were depicted inside buildings, and paintings have been discovered inside the pyramids and tombs. Paintings show banquets which included onions, and priests are often seen to be holding onions or covering altars with them. Of all the vegetables depicted by craftsmen of the time, onions are the only one to have been created in gold. Along with bread, onions feature quite frequently in illustrations from Egyptian times.

EYE-WATERING STUFF
Onions played an important role in the mummification of the dead. Traces of onions have been found in the pelvic and thorax regions of remains as well as being attached to the soles of the feet and legs. Other remains have

been discovered with onion pressed against the ears and bunches of flowering onions on their chests. Rameses IV was buried with onions in his eye sockets. One theory suggests that the Ancient Egyptians were aware of the antiseptic properties in onions that we value today. These would be useful in the afterlife. Another suggests that the Egyptians believed that the strong smell of onions would revive the dead. Luckily for Rameses IV this didn't happen, otherwise he would never have been able to stop crying!

UNRULY OXEN . . . OR ANGRY GODS?

The Sumerians, who lived in Mesopotamia around 2500 BC, were the first people to develop inscriptions as a written language. Once such inscription has been translated, suggests that onions were considered worthy of special attention by those in positions of power or authority. An incident occurred where oxen apparently ploughed over a crop of onions and cucumbers belonging to the governor. He had used the land where the crop had been cultivated – a land described as 'the gods' best field', better known as the temple field – unofficially. Obviously the governor had got a bit above himself and expropriated the land for himself. Perhaps it was the intervention of the gods or someone who knew their onions.

CHINESE ALLIUMS

Onions were growing in China 5,000 years ago and garlic was welcomed around 2700 BC, when it was used in banquet dishes for flavouring. In later times garlic was used to help preserve food and by around 200 BC it was recorded as one of over 300 plants cultivated there. Today, garlic is thought to have warming, stimulating effects and is used to treat depression.

SELECTED USES

The Egyptians had thousands of remedies involving onions and garlic to alleviate ailments. Onions were fed, together with garlic, to workers building the pyramids. Herodotus, the Greek historian, suggested that 90 tons of gold were spent on supplying onions for workers while the pyramids were being built. Egyptian slave workers were given a daily ration of garlic, as it was generally believed to ward off illness and to increase strength and endurance. During the reign of King Tut, 15 pounds of garlic apparently would have bought a healthy male slave.

Eating onions was associated with food for the poor or lower classes. In Mesopotamia, the needy were given monthly rations of bread and onions and this became part of their basic diet. Perhaps onions were considered disagreeable by those who could afford the luxuries of other foods because of the smell. We have to remember that onions were eaten raw, so the stench on everyone's breath must have been quite overpowering. Still, the peasants were eating healthily and probably preventing a lot of ailments, if they did but know it. People in Pelusium, in Lower Egypt, worshipped the onion and would eat neither onions nor garlic.

FORBIDDEN FOOD

Onions seemed to take on a double role in Egypt. Bread, beer and onions were the staples eaten extensively by the poor, but some priests were forbidden to eat onions. The reason isn't clear, but you have to wonder if they were turned down as a food because they were so esteemed for ceremonies and rituals, or because the onion breath offended the ruling classes. Even today, however, in India some Brahmans are forbidden to eat onions or garlic, although their use in medicines is acceptable. In India, in the sixth century BC, onion was used as a medicine to treat problems with digestion, the heart, eyes and joints. It was also recognised as a diuretic.

ONIONS IN THE BIBLE

Onions are noted in the Bible as one of the foods most longed for by the Israelites. After the Jews escaped into the wilderness with Moses they lamented the lost luxuries of Egypt in Numbers 11:5:

> *We remember the fish, which we did eat in Egypt freely, the cucumbers and melons, and leeks and the onions and the garlic.*

HEBREW GARLIC

The ancient Hebrews believed that garlic eased hunger, gave colour to the complexion, improved blood circulation, killed parasites, cured jealousy, kept the body warm, and encouraged love. The Talmud, a book of ancient Hebrew teachings, encouraged eating garlic on a Friday before making love on the Sabbath as a good deed.

EATING ONIONS WITH RELISH

By 500 BC the ancient Greeks were happily devouring onions, along with peas, lentils and cabbages. Everyone could afford onions, even if they didn't run to a more varied diet of vegetables. The Greek physician Hippocrates (300 BC) prescribed onions as a diuretic, for healing wounds and fighting pneumonia and digestive disorders. Athletes were fed large quantities of onions, to improve their blood and fortify them. By the 1st century AD, Discorides, another eminent physician of the day, who travelled widely in Europe and the Near East, noted several uses for onions because of their medicinal properties. He praised garlic for use in treating heart problems. His work influenced Roman thinking, where gladiators were rubbed down with onions in an attempt to firm up the muscles. Onions were consumed as a juice as well as raw food.

HOLD THE GARLIC

The upper class Greeks didn't go for garlic in the same way, however. Anyone smelling of garlic was considered vulgar and was prevented from entering the temples. An often retold legend tells that they fed garlic to criminals in the belief that it would purge them of their crimes! In contrast, Aristotle listed garlic among the foods he considered aphrodisiacs. Garlic had its uses in other ways: in Aristophanes' play, *Wives at the Feast of Thesmophores*, the women who were cheating on their husbands found garlic the perfect cover-up for a night of indiscretion.

STRONG TASTES

Alexander the Great (356–323 BC) fed onions to his armies when they were out busy plundering. The idea was that if you ate strongly flavoured food you would become stronger. Scientific research has come up with a lot of reasons why onions are good for you, but they don't have a lot to do with physical strength. Mind you, the antiseptic qualities probably came in handy.

SENSITIVE NOSES AND STOMACHS

Horace the Roman poet (65 BC—8 BC) recorded his hatred of garlic, which he called 'more poisonous than hemlock'. He claimed it once made him ill at the table of his benefactor, Maecenas. People who ate garlic were not allowed into the temple of Cybele. Garlic has many more associations with rituals and superstitions, which you can read about in a separate chapter. Not everyone thought garlic was a bad thing, however, and Pliny gave a long list of maladies which could be cured with a bit of garlic

DOES MY BREATH SMELL?

Meanwhile, back in Rome, the poor were eating onions with gusto. The better off, however, were not so keen. In Pompeii, destroyed by volcanic activity in AD 79, onion sellers were not included in a guild of vegetable and flower sellers because they were lower in class terms. It is curious, therefore, that archaeologists have unearthed a basket of cooked onions from inside one of the city brothels. Onions were obviously held in higher esteem when the elite mixed with more lowly, earthy women — or maybe the men just went there for the onions. Another theory could suggest that if you have to breathe the smell of stale onions, you might as well be immune by smelling the same yourself!

ROMAN SATIRISTS AND POETS

Onions and garlic didn't escape the notice of at least two poets and satirists of the Roman era. Juvenal, who was writing in the first century, described the Egyptians' strange relationship with onions. Translated, it reads:

> *How Egypt, mad with superstition grown*
> *Makes gods of monsters but too well is known*
> *'Tis mortal sin an onion to devour*
> *Each clove of garlic hath a sacred power*

Another poet, Martial, wrote in 80 AD:

He who bears chives on his breath
Is safe from being kissed to death

ROASTED ONIONS
By the beginning of the second century AD onions were getting a better press in Rome and strings of onions were displayed in markets. The Romans took their onions on journeys to Britain and Germany. Pliny the Elder (AD 23–79) had recorded that onions and cabbages were available in Pompeii and he wrote about how onions and garlic could help with over 60 remedies to restore poor vision, help induce sleep, heal sores and dog bites, soothe toothache and help fight dysentery. He wrote of the gardens where onions were grown in special beds, called *cepinae*. The gardeners who cared for them were named *ceparii*, and archaeologists have since found holes in the ground where the onions were destroyed by the ash and heat. Pliny, who himself perished at Pompeii, listed many varieties of onions which were mostly identified by their place of origin. The Cypress onion was strong and the mildest came from Cnidos. The smallest was from Tuscany and the whitest onions grew at Issus and Sardis. He also described those with the roundest shape as the best and noted that red onions were more pungent than white ones.

ONIONS OR HONEY WITH YOUR TOAST?
Apicius, the great writer on food and author in the late 4th and early 5th century AD, only used onions for flavouring sauces or to add to a mixed dressing or salad dish. Onions never featured in dishes for the wealthy classes. Imagine starting your day with a slice of bread, covered with raw onions instead of honey: or perhaps not!

HEADACHE CURE
By the Middle Ages onions had become such an important food that they would be given as gifts or used to pay bills and tithes. The account book of Henry de Lacy, Earl of Lincoln in Holbourne for 1295–96, lists, for the purpose of tithing:

Of 4s. 1 ¼ d for onions and garlick sold, the tithe
being deducted.

His expenses included
> *17s. 0½ d in 1500 onions.*

In medieval times the kitchen garden was sometimes called the leek garden and the gardener was known as the leek-ward. Leeks were much prized by Edward I, whose gardener, in 1290, was told to 'Find worts from Michaelmas to Lent and leeks throughout Lent'. Leeks were later planted in the grounds of Westminster Abbey, in 1321. French priests of the Middle Ages used garlic to protect themselves from bubonic plague.

Beans, cabbages and onions were well known throughout Europe. John Gardener recorded in *A Feat of Gardening* (*c.*1400) that onions should be planted around Valentine's Day, as they are hardy plants. Onions were prescribed by doctors for the treatment of headaches, hair loss and snake bites, amongst other things. Countless folk remedies recommended their curative powers, such as putting a sliced onion under your pillow to fight off insomnia. It would certainly fight other bedfellows off!

Garlic was also mentioned in several plant collections, although it was unknown in its present form at that time in Britain. The name garlic comes from the Anglo-Saxon words *gar*, meaning spear, and *lac*, meaning a plant, because of the shape of its leaves. Many writers praised garlic for its medicinal uses, while others remained sceptical. Alexander Neckam, a 12th century writer, recommended garlic for heatstroke amongst field labourers.

LEEKS AND THE WELSH
Most people associate leeks with Wales. The tradition of wearing a leek on St David's Day comes from the 6th century, when King Cadwallader directed his troops to identify themselves in a battle against the Saxons. Legend has it that the battle took place in a leek field and the emblem was used to distinguish them from the Saxons. Whether this is true or not, the leek has long been a symbol for Wales. Between 1985 and 1990 the British pound coin bore a design including a leek.

MOLE WRENCH

In medieval times there was some superstition and worry about using herbs because of their association with pagan rites and magic, and the Catholic Church discouraged the use of some herbs. The art of growing and using herbs for medicine was called '*Simpling*'. In Cole's *Art of Simpling*, he suggested that if you had a problem with moles in the garden, 'Garlic or leeks will make them leap out of the ground presently.' He also described cocks which had been fed on garlic as 'most stout to fight, and so are Horses'. I don't think he meant for them to be fighting each other, though.

TUDOR SENSE OF HUMOUR

In Tudor times, theories of health revolved around the four humours or fluids. These were blood, phlegm, yellow bile and black bile. If the humours were imbalanced you became ill. Onions giving a hot flavour were thought to be particularly useful. Onions were prescribed by doctors to help with infertility in women and even in dogs, cattle and many other household pets. Thomas Hill, in *The Gardener's Labyrinth* (1577), wrote:

> *Garlike putteth away inward swellings, openeth*
> *impostumes, killeth lice and nits of the head,*
> *moveth urine, helpeth toothach proceeding from*
> *a cold cause.*

John Gerard, famous botanist and writer of the times, was quite dismissive of both onions and garlic. Perhaps his treatment of garlic is more understandable, since only wild varieties would have been available at the time. While garlic later became a popular vegetable throughout southern Europe, it was never fully embraced by the British, although it is said to have been growing in Britain before 1548.

John Gerard's *Herball* (1597) commented on garlic in the following text:

Allium sylvestre: Of Crow-Garlicke and Ramsons.

> *The leaves of Ramsons be stamped and eaten of*
> *dinners in the Low-countries, with fish for a*

sauce, even as we do eat greene-sauce made with sorrell. The same leaves may very well be eaten in April and May with butter, of such as are of a strong constitution, and labouring men.

This is more tolerant than the following words on onions:

The Onion being eaten, yea though it be boyled, causeth head-ache, hurteth the eyes, and maketh a man dimme sighted, dulleth the sences, ingendreth windinesse, and provoketh overmuch sleepe, especially being eaten raw . . . There is also another small kinde of Onion, called . . . Scallions . . . It is used to be eaten in sallads.

Gerard listed several varieties including a white onion, flattened in shape, the red Onion 'which differth not from the former but in sharpnesse and rednesse of the root,' and the Spanish kind, which has a longer, more oval root.

Parkinson's description of onions in 1629 agreed with Gerard.

We have divers sorts of Onions, both white and red, flat, round and long. The red flat kinde is most usually with us the strongest of them all.

He also described a red onion that he obtained from overseas that was twice the size of a man's fist, red throughout and pleasant to both smell and eat. He described white and Spanish onions as long and flat,

'very sweete, and eaten by many like an apple.'

I think I'll pass on that suggestion.

Astrology also played a part in Tudor medicine. Most doctors believed that different signs ruled different parts of the body. Maybe this accounts also for plants being attributed to different planets. Nicholas Culpeper, herbalist at the start of the 17th century, admitted to leaving out chives altogether in his original work.

Government and virtues: I confess I had not added these, had it not been for a country gentleman, who by a letter certified me, that amongst other herbs, I had left these out; they are indeed a kind of leek, hot and dry in the fourth degree as they are, and so under the dominion of Mars; if they be eaten raw, (I do not mean raw, opposite to roasted or boiled, but raw, opposite to chymical preparation) they send up very hurtful vapours to the brain, causing troublesome sleep, and spoiling the eye-sight, yet of them prepared by the art of the alchymist, may be made an excellent remedy for the stoppage of the urine.

He was much more a fan of garlic for medical uses:

The offensiveness of the breath of him that hath eaten Garlick, will lead you by the nose to the knowledge hereof, and (instead of a description) direct you to the place where it grows in gardens, which kinds are the best, and most physical.

Government and virtues: Mars owns this herb. This was anciently accounted the poor man's treacle, it being a remedy for all diseases and hurts (except those which itself breed.) It provokes urine, and women's courses, helps the biting of mad dogs and other venomous creatures, kills worms in children, cuts and voids tough phlegm, purges the head, helps the lethargy, is a good preservative against, and a remedy for any plague, sore, or foul ulcers; takes away spots and blemishes in the skin, eases pains in the ears, ripens and breaks imposthumes, or other swellings. And for all those diseases the onions are as effectual.

But the Garlick hath some more peculiar virtues besides the former, viz. it hath a special quality to discuss inconveniences coming by corrupt agues or mineral vapours; or by drinking corrupt and stinking waters; as also by taking wolfbane, henbane, hemlock, or other poisonous and dangerous herbs. It is also held good in hydropick diseases, the jaundice, falling sickness, cramps, convulsions, the piles or hæmorrhoids, or other cold diseases.

Many authors quote many diseases this is good for; but conceal its vices. Its heat is very vehement, and all vehement hot things send up but ill-favoured vapours to the brain. In coleric men it will add fuel to the fire; in men oppressed by melancholy, it will attenuate the humour, and send up strong fancies, and as many strange visions to the head; therefore let it be taken inwardly with great moderation; outwardly you may make more bold with it.

Of onions, Culpeper wrote:

Government and virtues: Mars owns them, and they have gotten this quality, to draw any corruption to them, for if you peel one, and lay it upon a dunghill, you shall find it rotten in half a day, by drawing putrefaction to it; then, being bruised and applied to a plague sore, it is very probable it will do the like.

Onions are flatulent, or windy; yet they do somewhat provoke appetite, increase thirst, ease the belly and bowels, provoke women's courses, help the biting of a mad dog, and of other venomous creatures, to be used with honey and rue, increase sperm, especially the seed of them. They also kill worms in children if they drink the water fasting wherein they have been steeped all night. Being roasted under the embers, and eaten with honey or sugar and oil, they much conduce to help an inveterate cough, and expectorate the tough phlegm.

The juice being snuffed up into the nostrils, purges the head, and helps the lethargy, (yet the often eating them is said to procure pains in the head). It hath been held by divers country people

*a great preservative against infection to eat
Onions fasting with bread and salt. As also to
make a great Onion hollow, filling the place with
good treacle, and after to roast it well under the
embers, which, after taking away the outermost
skin thereof, being beaten together, is a
sovereign salve for either plague or sore, or any
other putrefied ulcer. The juice of Onions is good
for either scalding or burning by fire, water, or
gunpowder, and used with vinegar, takes away all
blemishes, spots and marks in the skin: and
dropped in the ears, eases the pains and noise of
them. Applied also with figs beaten together,
helps to ripen and break imposthumes, and other
sores.*

*Leeks are as like them in quality, as the pome-
water is like an apple. They are a remedy against
a surfeit of mushrooms, being baked under the
embers and taken, and being boiled and applied
very warm, help the piles. In other things they
have the same property as the Onions, although
not so effectual.*

So, what are we waiting for? Why spend money on
medicines when alliums can cure practically every known
17th century ailment. Next time there's a flu (or plague)
epidemic, I might try hollowing out an onion, filling it
with treacle and roasting it before mashing it together
and eating it. You can read about some more modern
ideas and benefits to health in the next chapter.

THAT'S SHALLOT!
Shallots were becoming more popular in England by the
18th century and could be found in kitchen gardens
everywhere. They were used a lot in sauces. One
gardener, called Batty Langley, recommended a border:

*Four feet wide and about thirty five or forty feet
long is sufficient for a very large family.*

That's a lot of sauce!

ALLIUMS IN THE AMERICAS

The onion was introduced to North America by Christopher Columbus on his expedition to Haiti in 1493, when he took the first cultivated varieties to the New World.Their popularity quickly spread among Native American cultures.

Later, the first Pilgrims took onions with them on the *Mayflower*. However, they found that strains of wild onions already grew throughout North America. Native American Indians used wild onions in a variety of ways, eating them raw or cooked, as a seasoning or as a vegetable. Onions were also used in syrups, as poultices, for dyeing and even as toys. According to diary entries from the period, bulb onions were planted as soon as the Pilgrim Fathers could clear the land in 1648.

CHICAGO, THE BIG ONION

The city of Chicago was named after a variety of onion that Native American Indians used. The region grew wild onions in abundance and received its name from the Indian word that described the odour of onions.

UNPOPULAR GARLIC

The wild onions already growing in America didn't compare with the intensely flavoured European varieties. Garlic was brought to the Americas by the Spanish. The explorer Cortes planted garlic in Mexico and noted even the Indians of Peru took a fancy to the herb. Indians throughout the continent quickly adopted these new onions with great enthusiasm, especially the garlic, although garlic has never been as popular as onions in the USA. Leeks were found more often in the gardens of the well-off or those who liked to experiment a bit in their gardens.

In 1821 William Cobbett wrote in *The American Gardener*:

> Almost all nations except the English, the Americans, and the French, make great and constant use of Garlick; and, even the French use it, frequently, to an extent that would drive us from the table.

(My worst experiences in France have been not at tables nor in restaurants, but on crowded *Metro* trains — enough to make anyone hang from one of the straps!)

Although garlic was consumed with passion throughout the rest of the world, many Americans considered its odour offensive and socially unacceptable. During the early part of the 20th century some cooks would season their foods with only minute amounts of garlic salt or garlic powder. Many well-respected cooks omitted garlic in dishes, substituting onions instead. Gradually, because of the influx of European immigrants to America, garlic slowly acquired an acceptable reputation, when Jewish and Italian newcomers introduced their cuisines. Along with traditional foods they brought folk remedies, many that relied on garlic to cure everything.

CIVIL WAR
During the Civil War, General Ulysses S. Grant, who led the Union forces, sent a note to the War Department that read, 'I will not move my troops without onions'. The reply came in the form of three cartloads of onions. As well as feeding onions to the soldiers, Grant employed the juice of onions medicinally as a healer of wounds.

STEW ON THAT
American cowboys apparently favoured the prairie onion, which they called skunk egg, no doubt because of its powerful odour. Onions were always included in a favourite cowboy dish called, rather in the Wild West style, Son-of-a-bitch Stew. Hmmm, must find a recipe for that!

NEW INDUSTRY
During World War II, the US government appealed to farmers to produce dehydrated garlic and onions that could be shipped overseas with food supplies for the troops. A group of Californian farmers responded and planted a few acres of garlic, which began a successful commercial venture. Today, Gilroy in California calls itself 'Garlic Capital of the United States'.

ONION LAW

Some strange legislation has evolved over the years in the USA, but one law in Nacogdoches, Texas forbids young women from indulging in eating raw onion after 6 p.m. Why only young women?

VICTORIAN TIMES

Peter Adam Schenk records, in *The Gardener's Text-book* (1857), the wisdom of Sir John Sinclair who wrote: 'It is a well known fact, that a Highlander with a few raw onions in his pocket, and a crust of bread or bit of cake, can work or travel to an almost incredible extent for two or three days together.' He wouldn't be troubled by idle passers-by wanting to stop and chat either.

TWENTIETH CENTURY ONIONS

Garlic was in great demand as an antiseptic during past wars. In World War I, British doctors used a juice of raw garlic diluted with water and applied it directly to wounds to control infections. In 1916 the Government encouraged the growing of garlic by offering one shilling per pound for as much as could be produced. Each pound generally represents about 20 bulbs. Five pounds divided up into cloves and planted would hopefully yield about 38 pounds at the end of the season.

After the discovery of penicillin in 1928 garlic was used less as an antibiotic, but requirements during World War II overwhelmed demand and garlic was used again to control infections. The Red Army physicians relied so heavily on garlic that it became known as the 'Russian Penicillin'. Onions were also applied to battle wounds as an antiseptic. Onions and garlic were also fed to the troops to increase resistance to infection.

Nutritional
Alliums

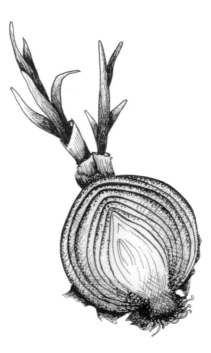

Garlick maketh a man wynke, drynke, and stynke.
(Thomas Nashe, 16th-century poet)

The benefits to health and nutrition to be gained from eating alliums have long been known. Throughout history, onions and garlic have been considered herbal wonders, with a reputation in folklore for preventing everything from the common cold to major infections. Many of the old claims have been put to the test by scientific research in more modern times and the sometimes unusual claims have often been proved to be true. There is still a debate on some properties, however, so the following information should not be considered as a substitute for expert medical advice. Most people would agree that eating alliums is good for you in general terms of nutrition and staying healthy.

As you can see from the following table that I have compiled from a variety of sources, although onions, garlic and leeks all belong to the same family, there is quite a difference between nutritional values of vitamin and mineral content. This table is approximate only, because various organisations give values for different quantities, i.e. a small onion (how small?), a leek (they vary a bit), 100 grams or a cupful. Confused? You're not the only one.

COMPARISON OF NUTRIENTS BETWEEN 100G RAW ONIONS, RAW GARLIC AND RAW LEEKS

NUTRIENT		ONIONS	GARLIC	LEEKS
Vitamin K		0.4 mcg	1.4 mg	47 mcg
Vitamin C		7.4 mg	31 mg	17 mg
Vitamin E		0.02 mg	0.01 mg	0.92 mg
Vitamin B	Thiamin	0.046 mg	0.2 mg	0.056 mg
	Riboflavin	0.027 mg	0.11 mg	0.033 mg
	Niacin	0.116 mg	0.7 mg	0.4 mg
	Folate	19 mcg	4 mcg	56 mcg
B6	Pyridoxine	0.119 mg	1.23 mg	0.48 mg
Iron		1.48 mg	1.7 mg	1.1 mg
Magnesium		0.129 mg	25 mg	28 mg
Manganese		0.16 mg	1.7 mg	0.43 mg
Potassium		146 mg	401 mg	180 mg
Copper		0.08 mg	0.3 mg	0.11 mg
Calcium		23 mg	181 mg	60 mg
Phosphorus		29 mg	153 mg	34.8 mg
Zinc		0.17 mg	1.16 mg	0.12 mg
Sodium		4 mg	17 mg	20 mg

Abbreviations

g	= gram
mg	= milligram
mcg	= microgram

Leeks are particularly good for magnesium, vitamin C and folate. Garlic is rich in vitamin C, potassium, phosphorus and calcium. Onions are just good for you. In a medium sized onion (148 grams) there are approximately 60 calories and:

Water	130 g
Carbohydrates	14 g
Protein	2 g
Dietary fibre	3 g
Phosphorus	32 mg
Potassium	200 mg
Sodium	5 mg

Food values can be deceptive, however. Bear in mind when looking at the table below that a medium-sized onion is more than 100 grams and that you are not likely to use 100 grams of garlic in any one meal. I found the calorific content of garlic quite a surprise, but it makes up for itself in terms of protein and carbohydrate value.

COMPARISON OF FOOD VALUES FOR ONIONS, LEEKS AND GARLIC, PER 100 GRAMS

Per 100 g	RAW ONIONS	LEEKS	GARLIC
Calories	36	22	149
Carbohydrate	9.3 g	2.9 g	33 g
Protein	1.3 g	1.6 g	6.36 g
Water	84 g	90.8 g	59 g

COMPARISON OF NUTRITIONAL VALUES FOR EATING ONIONS, PER AVERAGE ONION

Per average ONION	RAW	FRIED IN OIL	PICKLED IN VINEGAR
Energy (Kcal)	54	66	4
Protein (grams)	1.8	0.9	0.1
Carbohydrate (grams)	11.9	5.9	0.7
Sodium (milligrams)	5	2	68
Calcium (milligrams)	38	19	3

This may be useful, or if not, mildly interesting. Most people don't bother about the nutritional value of pickled onions, but watch out if you are on a restricted sodium diet! Of course, there will be more than one onion to the quantity of raw or fried ones, which racks up the amount.

THE C TO Z OF
MINERALS AND VITAMINS IN ALLIUMS

CALCIUM
Both magnesium and calcium are needed for healthy bones. Calcium is essential for the normal growth and maintenance of bones and teeth. Requirements must be met throughout life, with long-term calcium deficiency leading to an increasing occurrence of osteoporosis, particularly among women over 50, in which bones deteriorate and there is an increased risk of fractures.

CHROMIUM
Onions are very rich in chromium, a trace mineral that helps cells respond to insulin, plus vitamin C and numerous flavonoids, especially quercitin (see below).

IRON
Iron is found in every cell in the body. Iron links with protein to form haemoglobin, which is the oxygen transporter in your blood. Iron keeps your immune system healthy and helps to produce energy. Insufficient iron leads to anaemia.

MAGNESIUM
Helps to regulate the nerve and muscle tone. Magnesium keeps the muscles relaxed by preventing calcium entering the nerve cells. Insufficient magnesium may lead to muscle spasms or cramps, migraine, high blood pressure and fatigue.

MANGANESE
Manganese is an essential mineral trace element. Its name comes from the Greek word for magic. Manganese is an antioxidant that is important in the breakdown of amino acids and the production of energy. It activates

various enzymes which are important for proper digestion of foods. It helps break down cholesterol and feeds the nerves and brain. It is necessary for normal skeletal development, maintaining sex hormone production, and for regulating blood sugar levels.

PHOSPHORUS
Phosphorus is a mineral that makes up 1% of the total body weight. It is present in every cell of the body, but 85% of the body's phosphorus is found in the bones and teeth. It plays an important role in the body's use of carbohydrates and fats and in the synthesis of protein for the growth, maintenance and repair of cells and tissues. It is also crucial for the production of a molecule the body uses to store energy. Phosphorus works with the B vitamins. It assists in the contraction of muscles, in kidney function, in maintaining the regularity of the heartbeat, and in nerve conduction. The main food sources are the protein food groups of meat and milk but there are small quantities in green vegetables. A meal plan that provides adequate amounts of calcium and protein also provides an adequate amount of phosphorus.

POTASSIUM
Potassium helps to contract all the muscles in the body. It is essential for heart function and maintaining normal blood pressure. Studies have shown that potassium reduces blood pressure and the risk of strokes.

SELENIUM
Selenium is present as a trace element. It may help prevent cancer by acting as an antioxidant.

SODIUM
Sodium is an element that the body needs to function properly and occurs naturally in most foods. The body uses sodium to regulate blood pressure and blood volume. Sodium is also critical for the functioning of muscles and nerves. Onions contain sodium naturally, as does drinking water, although the amount varies depending on the source.

SULPHUR

Sulphur is an essential component of all living cells and is absorbed by plants from the soil. Onions are not as strong as garlic when it comes to sulphur compounds. In fact, garlic contains four times as much as onions. In plants and animals the amino acids cysteine and methionine contain sulphur, as do all proteins, and enzymes which contain these amino acids. In all there are 32 sulphur compounds identified in garlic and 17 amino acids. Allicin is one of these compounds (see below).

In general, a stronger tasting clove of garlic has more sulphur content. Some people have suggested that organically grown garlic has a higher sulphur level and hence greater benefit to health, but I can't comment on that — although I grow my vegetables organically, I've never managed to grow garlic successfully!

VITAMIN BC, FOLATE

Folic acid is known as folate in its natural form. If you are intending to become pregnant — or are pregnant already — you should take a daily supplement from the time you stop using contraception until the 12th week of pregnancy. Folates are also used to treat anaemia.

VITAMIN B3, NIACIN

Niacin helps the body turn the food we eat into energy. It also helps keep the nervous and digestive systems healthy.

VITAMIN B6, PYRIDOXINE

Pyridoxine is part of the B6 group vitamins and is water-soluble. It is required for both mental and physical health. It is needed for balancing hormonal changes in women, assisting the immune system and the growth of new cells. It is also used in the processing of proteins, fats and carbohydrates. It helps to control mood and behaviour. Pyridoxine is also thought to be of benefit for children with learning difficulties, as well as assisting in the prevention of skin complaints. It helps to promote red blood cell production and has been linked to cancer immunity and preventing heart disease.

VITAMIN C

Vitamin C is the main water-soluble antioxidant in the body and is vital for the healthy functioning of the immune system. It is good at preventing common colds and may also help to reduce recurrent ear infections. Vitamin C helps vitamin E become active and is associated with reducing inflammation caused by asthma and arthritis. It is also particularly effective in combating free-radical formation caused by pollution and cigarette smoke.

VITAMIN E

Vitamin E is the body's main fat-soluble antioxidant. It plays a big role in preventing cardiovascular disease and is one of the main antioxidants found in cholesterol. It helps prevent free radicals that would damage the cell membranes by oxidising the cholesterol. If cholesterol is oxidised it causes problems by sticking to blood vessel walls and blocking arteries.

VITAMIN K

Vitamin K is responsible for maintaining healthy bones. It activates osteocalcin, which is a major bone protein. As it is fat soluble you don't need to have it every day. Any of this vitamin your body doesn't need immediately is stored in the liver for future use. Vitamin K has other important functions, for example helping wounds to heal properly by clotting the blood.

ZINC

Zinc is second only to iron in its concentration in the body. The body needs zinc for the immune system to work properly. It plays a role in cell division, cell growth, wound healing, and the breakdown of carbohydrates. Zinc is also needed for the senses of smell and taste. Most zinc is consumed through high-protein foods such as meat and fish. Low-protein diets and vegetarian diets tend to be low in zinc.

BENEFICIAL COMPOUNDS FOUND IN ALLIUMS

Alliums contain a number of compounds that have health benefits. The actual effects on health will depend on whether the onions and garlic you eat are raw and, if cooked, how they are prepared. Also, there is quite a difference between varieties of onions, leeks and garlic. Science has shown that garlic and onions contain powerful antibiotics, so their use before the introduction of such antibiotics as penicillin holds up under the microscope. The human body does not appear to build up resistance to garlic, like some modern antibiotics, so positive health benefits continue over time.

FLAVONOIDS

Some of the beneficial compounds identified in alliums are called flavonoids and are most commonly known for activity as antioxidants. They are sometimes referred to as bioflavonoids, because they are biological in origin. Interest in them has grown for their medicinal potential in preventing cancers and heart disease. They seem to work by modifying bodily reactions to viruses, allergens and cancer producing agents, showing antimicrobial, anti-inflammatory and anti-cancer activity. Other foods high in flavonoids include tea, red wine and broccoli.

Flavonoids on their own are of little direct antioxidant value and are not absorbed well by the body, but it is thought that they work by increasing uric acid levels. The body treats them as foreign compounds which it wants to get rid of as quickly as it can. At the same time it gets rid of other unwanted compounds and increases the antioxidant capacity of the blood.

There are two main groups of flavonoids in alliums, which are called anthocyanins and flavonols.

QUERCETIN

Quercetin is one type of flavonol, found to be the most active of the flavonoids. Many medicinal plants owe a lot of their benefits to their high quercetin content. Quercetin creates anti-inflammatory activity by inhibiting several initial processes of inflammation, such as the release of histamine. In addition, it is a powerful antioxidant. Quercetin is said to be more prevalent in yellow and red onions than in white varieties.

ANTHOCYANINS

These flavonoids are prevalent in the pigment of a variety of plants, fruit and vegetables. Anthocyanin is the pigment responsible for making red cabbage different from other varieties, but it is not the pigment in beetroot.

ALLICIN

Garlic contains allicin, a strong antibacterial compound which is yielded when the garlic is crushed. Alliin, an amino acid found in alliums, is converted into allicin. Considered a key compound in the past, more recent research suggests that allicin is not biologically active inside the body. Allicin is what makes garlic smell and what prevents insects and fungi eating or attacking it. This defence system is a sort of natural insecticide. Put simply, allicin breaks down into sulphide compounds which smell, so this is why alliums stink!

Allicin has a powerful antimicrobial property but because it cannot be absorbed easily, it has never been adopted commercially. As well as all that, the smell of garlic is not appreciated by everyone. Allicin is responsible for the hot, burning flavour of fresh garlic and is only activated by chemical reaction once garlic is chopped or crushed. It is unstable and is rapidly destroyed by cooking. However, the idea that it has the ability to dissolve fats has been questioned recently.

Beneficial
Alliums

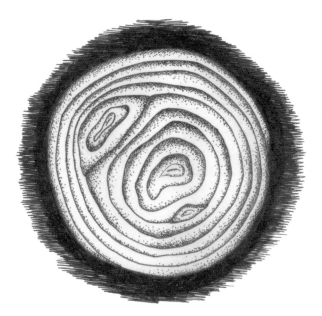

CONDITIONS THAT
MAY BE HELPED BY EATING ALLIUMS

*Garlic gives health both to the well and the ill. It ought
to be eaten uncooked, because if it is cooked,
its strength is lost.*

Hildegarde von Bingen, healer and 12th-century Abbess

Onions contain chemicals that help fight the free radicals
in our bodies. These free radicals cause disease and
destruction to cells and have been linked to at least 60
diseases. The benefits were known to our ancestors, who
used them to protect against a range of ailments,
illnesses and infections.

Garlic has been used as an antidote to poison, and as a
diuretic and a stimulant. People have used garlic to treat
asthma, coughs, lung disorders and chilblains. Apparently,
Eleanor Roosevelt swallowed three chocolate-coated
garlic pills daily to aid her memory, but I don't remember
hearing that myself!

There are various garlic supplements available on the
market and garlic pills may have the added benefit of not
smelling. Be aware that the huge variety of products will
contain varying amounts of beneficial compounds and
that some of them are much more expensive than others:
certainly more expensive than eating fresh garlic.

Some claims seem a little more far-fetched than others,
like the use of garlic to treat cattle with anthrax, but
others, such as claims to combat certain bacteria, are
well researched and found to be effective.

Once again, I don't claim to have any medical expertise,
so you should consult your doctor first if in doubt about
any symptoms. Eating garlic and onions should be seen
as part of a healthy lifestyle, not as an alternative cure.
It may also interfere with prescribed medicines, if taken
in large amounts or supplements.

If nothing else, the following information may encourage
you to eat alliums more often, or at least to use chives to
garnish a dish or two.

HEART DISEASE AND
ANTI-CHOLESTEROL PROPERTIES

Onions seem to be a useful vegetable for preventing cardiovascular disease because they reduce the risk of blood clots developing. They are thought to be helpful in fighting arteriosclerosis — or hardening of the arteries — when eaten regularly.

Garlic acts as a stimulant that warms the body and improves blood circulation because it contains arginine, a powerful antioxidant. This is an amino acid that helps to relax blood vessels. Aged garlic extract contains high levels of arginine and is created by soaking slices of garlic in aqueous ethanol for up to 20 months. This enhances the amino acid content and is the subject of several studies, in order to help patients with sickle-cell anaemia.

BLOOD PRESSURE, HEART ATTACK AND STROKE

Onions and garlic contain a number of sulphides which may lower blood lipids and blood pressure. It is interesting to note that in India, some communities who had never eaten onions or garlic, had higher cholesterol levels and shorter blood clotting times than other communities who ate substantial amounts of both onions and garlic.

The flavonoids in onions are known to provide protection against heart problems. Sulphur, along with chromium and vitamin B6, helps to prevent heart attacks and strokes. Onions have been highlighted in several studies of the vegetables and fruit that contribute to a significant reduction in heart disease, along with tea, apples and broccoli, the richest sources of flavonoids. Together they offer up to 20% reduction in the risk of heart disease. Incidentally, beetroot is also good for reducing the risk.

BLOOD THINNING

The anti-clotting effects are related to their sulphur content and this stops platelets clumping together. Garlic can thin the blood, just like aspirin, so if you are having general surgery or dental surgery and you like to overindulge in garlic, check with your doctor, especially if you have a bleeding disorder, or are taking drugs like aspirin regularly. Garlic has been shown to interfere with the effectiveness of a drug used to treat HIV infection and its interaction with other drugs is still under review.

BLOOD SUGAR

During some glucose-tolerance tests evidence was found to suggest that the higher the intake of onion, the lower the level of glucose. It has been suggested that one of the sulphides is responsible for this effect and that it lowers blood sugar levels by increasing the amount of free insulin available. It does this by competing with insulin to occupy the sites in the liver where insulin is not activated. An increase in the amount of insulin available to usher glucose into cells causes a lowering of blood sugar. Onions are a good source of chromium, which helps cells respond appropriately to insulin. Chromium levels are depleted by refined sugars and lack of exercise. If you want to restore your chromium levels, it has been suggested that a cup of raw onion a day will provide 20% of the daily recommended intake, but I wouldn't like to suggest such a thing myself. If you eat a balanced diet that is low in fat, salt and sugar and high in fresh fruit and vegetables, there won't be a problem.

DIABETES

Claims have been made that taking chromium and cinnamon can be of benefit to people with Type 2 Diabetes. There is no way at the moment of reversing this condition. As one of the growing breed of sufferers, I'm content to stick with the healthy diet and exercise routine, thank you. That includes eating lots of onions, garlic, broccoli, spinach and some beetroot. I won't be trying supplements. People taking insulin for Type 1 Diabetes should not consume medicinal amounts of garlic without consulting a physician.

LOWERING THE RISK OF SOME CANCERS

STRONG FLAVOURS ARE MORE BENEFICIAL
Researchers have discovered that members of the onion family with the strongest flavour, particularly New York Bold, Western Yellow and shallots, are the best varieties for inhibiting the growth of liver and colon cancer cells. Stronger flavoured onions could be more effective than their milder varieties. An analysis of ten common onion varieties and shallots was made for total antioxidant activity and their ability to fight the growth of cancer in human cells. Fresh, uncooked samples were used, with the outer skin removed. Tests showed that onions were better at prohibiting the growth of colon cancer than liver cancer. Sweeter tasting varieties, such as Vidalia, showed less ability to fight cancer cells. Shallots had six times more phenols (aromatic, chemical compounds) than mild onion varieties. You can find out more about varieties in a later chapter.

ANTIOXIDANTS
The antioxidants in fruits and vegetables, teas and wines have been identified and alliums are important species, possessing the ability to protect the body from damage caused by free radical-induced oxidative stress. Alliins can prevent the growth of malignant cells in animals and quercetin is also a powerful antioxidant and cancer-attacking agent. Ideally, onions and garlic should be eaten raw to get the most benefit. A study of the antioxidant activity of blue chives and their contents of total flavonoids, pigments, vitamin C and soluble proteins indicated that they exhibit antioxidant ability in all plant organs. The highest antioxidant ability was found in the leaves, so that's why a garnish of chives will do you good.

DON'T DITCH THE OUTER LAYERS
Another study into the dry outer skins of red, violet and yellow onions reported that free radical scavenging activity was most powerful in the outer layers. Quercetin has been found to reduce the level of an extremely powerful oxidant in the brain, by scavenging. It's a pity that the levels of antioxidants are at their highest in the very layers that we discard when cooking. Food for thought!

AN ONION A DAY . . .

There certainly seems to be a correlation between consumption of onions, shallots, garlic and leeks, and a lower incidence of stomach cancer. Countries where alliums are regularly consumed, such as Greece, have fewer deaths from stomach cancer. In China, the country with the highest intake of onions, garlic and other alliums, there is a 40% lower risk of stomach cancer than those with the lowest intake. Older people in the Netherlands with the highest onion consumption, estimated to eat at least half an onion a day, had half the level of stomach cancer compared with those consuming no onions at all. Eating onions two or three times a week is associated with a reduced risk of developing colon cancer. Quercetin has been shown to halt the growth of tumours in animals and to protect colon cells from damage. For instance, it has been suggested that cooking meats with onions may help reduce the amount of carcinogens produced when meat is cooked using high heat methods. So, if you have to have barbecues often in our long, hot summers — which we have had for some years now — eat onions with your hot dogs or burgers.

Studies in the USA have claimed impressive benefits from consuming alliums. People eating the most onions apparently showed an over 80% reduced risk of cancer of the oral cavity and pharynx, larynx and oesophagus. Over half of those studied had a reduced risk of colorectal cancer and a quarter had a reduced risk of breast cancer. Around three-quarters reduction in the risk of ovarian cancer and prostate cancer were also reported. Similarly, those eating the most garlic had reduced risks, but not as high as for onion eaters. This surprises me, because we are told that garlic has more punch than onions. Mind you, garlic has never been as popular in the States as in Europe. The problem with comparisons between popu-lations of other countries is that diets vary considerably and other environmental and cultural factors need to be taken into account. For example, the risk from some forms of cancer will be variable, depending on diet, healthy lifestyle and work.

GASTROINTESTINAL HEALTH

Quercetin and curcumin, which is also found in the curry spice turmeric, have been found to reduce both the size and number of precancerous lesions in the human intestine. A small number of patients with an inherited form of precancerous polyps in the lower bowel were treated with regular doses of curcumin and quercetin over an average of six months. The average number of polyps that did develop dropped by half. The condition can develop into cancer of the colon. Recently, anti-inflammatory drugs, such as aspirin, have been used to treat some patients with this condition, but often produce side effects. Studies of populations that consume large amounts of curry have strongly suggested that curcumin might be effective in preventing cancer in the lower intestine. Although the amount of quercetin was similar to what many people consume daily, the curcumin consumed was more than would be provided in a typical diet. While simply consuming curry and onions may not have a dramatic effect, research shows that liberal use of onions and turmeric can play a protective role against the development of colorectal cancer. Recent research suggests also that curcumin also plays a significant role in combating Alzheimer's disease.

BONES AND OSTEOPOROSIS

Onions, leeks and garlic may help reduce the risk of osteoporosis, the bone disease that affects one in three women, usually after the menopause, and some men. Milk has always been the obvious deliverer of calcium to the body, but adults don't drink as much milk as children. You might be pleased to know, however, that skimmed milk contains more calcium than semi-skimmed or whole milk, so that's a bonus to those of us on low fat diets. Onions came as quite a surprise on the list of foods I was given after a bone scan a few years ago.

Research on rats suggests that one gram of onion a day can help prevent the process that causes the condition, where calcium seeps from the bones and makes them brittle. A total of 500 milligrams of onion, mixed with garlic, lettuce, tomato, cucumber and parsley had just as good an effect. On a diet of onions, the rats developed stronger bones and effects could be seen within 12 hours.

Osteoporosis can cause the spine to bend and makes bones more likely to break. In the UK, 52,000 women alone suffer hip fractures each year. In economic terms it would appear that eating onions could save a lot of money on hospital treatment, as the population ages. Research is continuing with the rats, to identify which compounds in onions have the most positive effect, then to see if the effects are the same in humans. It appears that a compound shortened to GPCS stops the activity of osteoclasts, which are the cells that break down bone. We already know that eating too much salt can make matters worse. Salt raises blood pressure and speeds up the loss of calcium, leading to osteoporosis. Salt, remarkable though it is, also has a lot to answer for.

Another interesting fact I've discovered is that some drugs prescribed to prevent excessive bone loss, which work by destroying osteoclasts, may have side effects, including irritation of the upper gastrointestinal mucosa, acid regurgitation or oesophageal ulcers. Maybe having onion breath isn't so bad after all!

ANTI-INFLAMMATORY AND ANTIBACTERIAL EFFECTS

Onions also have anti-inflammatory effects. They relieve congestion in the airways. Throughout history onions have been used for relieving chest complaints. Native Americans and early settlers used wild onions to treat colds, coughs and asthma, and to repel insects. In Chinese medicine, onions have been used to treat angina, coughs, bacterial infections and breathing problems.

COUGHS AND COLDS
The World Health Organisation supports the use of onions for the treatment of poor appetite and for providing relief in the treatment of coughs and colds, asthma and bronchitis. Onions are known to decrease bronchial

spasms and an onion extract has been found to decrease allergy-induced bronchial constriction in patients who suffer from asthma and the congestion associated with the common cold. Quercetin and other flavonoids found in onions work with vitamin C, to help kill harmful bacteria. This makes sense of the old idea of feeding a cold. It also makes it worth adding onions, leeks and garlic to soups and stews during the cold and flu season.

For stopping a cold developing, one suggestion is to cut a large clove of garlic in half and hold it in your mouth for as long as possible: hours rather than minutes. Another remedy suggested to me when I was a teacher, surrounded by runny noses all day, was to swallow a whole clove of garlic in a spoonful of honey. I never did get round to trying that one either, although it would have kept the children away from me. Maybe I'll give it a try now that I work at home. At the beginning of the last century, Italian children were sometimes sent to school with necklaces of garlic cloves to prevent colds. A clove a day keeps the teacher at bay!

A Chinese cure for the common cold is to take 20 scallions (spring onions) and simmer them with rice to make porridge. Add vinegar to taste and eat while warm. Wrap the patient in a blanket and let the sweating begin.

OSTEO- AND RHEUMATOID ARTHRITIS
Several anti-inflammatory agents in onions help to reduce the severity of symptoms, such as the pain and swelling of osteo- and rheumatoid arthritis. Both onions and garlic contain compounds that inhibit the enzymes that generate inflammation, thus markedly reducing the effects. The anti-inflammatory effects are due to vitamin C, quercetin and other active components. A suggestion for relieving symptoms of rheumatism is to mix a clove or two with honey and consume for two or three consecutive nights.

ANTIBACTERIAL EFFECTS
Onions contain compounds that stimulate the growth of healthy bifidobacteria (the friendly bacteria we see on the adverts) and suppress the growth of potentially harmful bacteria in the colon.

Public health information in Russia apparently advises regular consumption of garlic and onions to prevent disease. Garlic is given as an inhalant to patients who have to stay in hospital. I suppose that's one way of discouraging visitors, who bring germs with them.

When garlic is eaten in large amounts it has a tendency to seep from the skin through sweat and breath, even the day after. This is because garlic's strong-smelling sulphur compounds are metabolised and cannot be digested. They are passed into the blood and carried to the lungs and the skin, where they are excreted. Digestion takes several hours, but the release of sulphur compounds takes several hours more, so the effect of eating garlic may be present for a long time.

Louis Pasteur is renowned for his work on discovering that microscopic germs cause infection. In 1858, Pasteur observed garlic's antibacterial properties. Decocted garlic extracts, i.e. garlic cloves boiled and left to set overnight, were found to be effective at killing bacteria under laboratory conditions. Garlic was used as an antiseptic to prevent gangrene during World War I and World War II. The raw garlic juice was put on sterilised sphagnum moss and placed directly onto wounds.

SKIN PROBLEMS

Garlic placed on the skin in this way, however, can cause irritation or worse in some people. Reports of serious burns resulting from garlic being applied topically for purposes including acne treatment need to be taken seriously, so I wouldn't like to try it myself. In many parts of the world, onions are still used to heal blisters and boils and, in the USA, products that contain onion extract are used in the treatment of topical scars. Perhaps that's why the British, when they first colonised India, noticed lepers eating garlic all the time. They called leprosy the 'peel garlic disease'.

REPELLING INSECTS

Garlic has a long history of getting rid of unwanted insects and other nasties, some of which are based more on superstition and folklore than science, but you can read about all that later on. Because it contains the powerful allicin compound mentioned earlier, garlic seems to offer protection from mosquito bites. I'm not so sure about vampires! It has been suggested that mosquitoes have evolved to avoid garlic and/or are overwhelmed and disorientated by the smell of the garlic so that they can't find a host.

So, if you have been eating masses of the stuff, to the extent that your skin smells of garlic, you may just persuade the evil biters to try their luck somewhere else, preferably miles away. I've often wondered why some people get eaten alive and others are left unscathed and have always put it down to hormones, but maybe garlic eaters are more protected.

A number of commercial garlic sprays on the market effectively coat an area and produce a natural barrier to insects. Let's just hope that bats (ordinary ones) who make fast food of the mosquitoes and midges around our garden don't have the same loathing as those aforementioned vampire varieties. There's also the proviso on sprays that, like leaves on railway lines, you are targeting the wrong sort. I find that lemon juice-based sprays work well on me but, when in France over the last couple of summers, everyone, including the garlic addicts, has got bitten to shreds, so I'm not totally convinced. I wouldn't want to rely entirely on garlic when travelling to destinations where malaria is endemic. One suggestion is to use a petroleum jelly-based product like Vaseline mixed with garlic juice, although you should be aware of the effects on sensitive skin, as in the section above. Another is to eat lots and sweat garlic. Lovely!

OTHER BENEFITS

- In homeopathic medicine, *Allium cepa* is used for treating hay fever.
- Garlic has been used as a treatment for intestinal worms and other intestinal parasites since early civilisations, both orally and (wince) as an anal suppository.
- Claims have been made that fungal infections such as

thrush can be improved by garlic. Whole cloves, used as vaginal suppositories, are sometimes used as a home remedy for yeast infections, but I wouldn't like to recommend it, or try it myself.

- Eating kale, onions and parsley is said to alleviate constipation. The allicin helps to stimulate the intestine.
- The ancient medical system used in India for centuries considered garlic too strong to be given to people with short tempers, because it could trigger anger or energetic imbalance. Garlic is known to have a stimulant effect in some cases.
- Chinese medicine places garlic in the category of warming and stimulating and it is prescribed for patients suffering from depression. Onions are thought to calm the liver and moisten the intestines. Raw onions are also prescribed for helping constipation.
- Garlic has been used as an antibacterial mouthwash.
- Uses as an animal medicine include treating animals infested with ticks and treating cattle with hoof and mouth diseases.
- The Romans would drink a solution of around 10 to 16 whole bulbs (not cloves) boiled down in a small bucket of wine for a hangover cure. Mmm, lovely!
- Garlic extract is said to be the vegetable version of Viagra, in stimulating aphrodisiacal properties. A study of rats given garlic supplements and a high protein diet saw the rats 'enjoying' boosted testosterone levels. Among practitioners of Ayurvedic medicine in India, garlic is regarded as an aphrodisiac and for its ability to fortify semen.
- In the 1950s, Russian workers suffering from lead poisoning were given daily doses of garlic. Their symptoms apparently eased. Similar studies in Japan found that garlic binds with heavy metals.
- An Italian remedy for stomach aches is to apply a poultice of garlic.
- To cure baldness, an old remedy suggests stirring three or four crushed bulbs into two pints of alcohol. I think the idea is to rub this into the scalp, but maybe you have to drink it. Maybe not.

UNWANTED EFFECTS

USE AND SAFETY

Onions are safely consumed by most people. However, consuming large quantities can lead to stomach distress and gastrointestinal irritation that may result in nausea and diarrhoea. I think you would have to eat a lot of onions for that to happen. During pregnancy and while breastfeeding, the consumption of garlic supplements and large quantities of garlic in food have been linked to a raised risk of bleeding. Needless to say, whatever you eat, the baby gets it as well, so expect a garlic odour to emanate from the baby, if you eat lots of garlic while breastfeeding.

ONIONS AND CRYING

The smelly sulphur compounds in onions and other alliums are primarily responsible for the flavour of onions and for producing the eye-irritating compounds that induce tears. As you slice an onion, cells are broken, allowing alliin enzymes to break down and generate acids which are unstable and decompose into a volatile gas. The gas disperses through the air and eventually reaches the eyes, where it reacts with the water to form a dilute solution of sulphuric acid. This irritant to the nerve endings in the eyes makes them sting. The tear glands then dilute and flush out the irritant by producing water in the form of tears.

There are several ways of trying to prevent the gas from reaching the eyes, although I can't say that any one method has ever worked with total success for me. I've even seen friends try to peel onions wearing goggles, which is amusing at least. When you take them off you have to make sure you don't have onion juice anywhere near your hands, so I suppose rubber gloves as well must be the answer. Then, of course, you'd have to remember to take off the gloves before removing the goggles, which is also tricky. My daughter tells me that kitchen hands in some restaurants and catering establishments are given goggles to wear when they have to prepare vast amounts of onions for mass catering — when she was a student she had to do it, but didn't shed any tears when she handed the goggles over to the next new recruit to the kitchen. Here are some other methods for avoiding red eyes and runny mascara:

- Take off the outer skins in a basin of water or under running water. Cut them in water.
- Rinse the onions and cut them on a board while still wet.
- Chilling or freezing can prevent the enzyme action and limit the gas produced.
- Use a sharp knife to speed up the process.
- Don't rub your eyes to get rid of the tears.
- Just grin and bear it. Sometimes a little cry can be quite therapeutic and induce sympathy.
- Get someone else to cut them for you! (I always try this first.)

The volume of acids released, and the irritation effect, differs between species and freshness of the onions. A firm in Canada once tried to use the properties of onions to make a form of tear gas in the 1990s. It was unsuccessful, as it had a very short, effective shelf life of three months.

GARLIC BREATH AND THE STINKING ROSE

Garlic breath is said to be alleviated by eating fresh parsley. This is, maybe, why the herb is included in many garlic recipes. However, eating parsley provides only a temporary masking, as the garlic stays in the system, as described above. One way of accelerating the release of compounds from the body is by having a sauna. Due to its strong odour, garlic is sometimes referred to as the 'stinking rose'. And the flowers are so pretty . . .

BOTULISM

Cases of botulism in the 1980s have been linked with consuming garlic-in-oil preparations that have not been treated properly. Botulism is characterised by blurred or double vision, speech and breathing difficulty and progressive paralysis.

Concerns about some outbreaks in the 1980s alerted manufacturers producing commercial products to the need for phosphoric or citric acid to be added as a microbial inhibitor when creating these mixtures. They should also be refrigerated to retard bacterial growth. The bacteria spores that cause botulism are widespread in nature, but they seldom cause problems because they can't grow if they are exposed to oxygen. However, when garlic containing the bacteria is covered with oil, there is no oxygen present. That means conditions are ripe for the spores to grow and produce toxins. You can slow down the growth of bacteria by refrigerating the product, so if you make garlic oil at home it must be refrigerated and eaten fresh, within one week. Never store garlic oil at room temperature. This way there will be no problem.

EFFECTS ON PRESCRIBED MEDICINES

These have already been mentioned, but again, check with your doctor before you try to help yourself with homeopathic remedies. Sometimes the effect of combining natural cures with prescription medicines is not good. Remember, too, that garlic is a blood-thinning agent, so you should not overindulge if you are on drugs to do the job already.

There are some people who are allergic to garlic. Symptoms include skin rashes, high temperatures, headaches and stomach cramps. I have one such friend and have become more aware over the years of the numbers of processed foods that contain garlic as an additive or flavouring. It makes cooking a meal quite interesting and curry especially challenging, but, thanks to the fact that onions are okay for her to eat, we get by.

Superstition, Folklore & Trivia

> *'Eat leeks in March and garlic in May,*
> *Then the rest of the year, your doctor can play.'*
> Old Welsh saying

Garlic has always, it seems, had a special place in folklore. From the times of the ancient Egyptians, when onions and garlic were worshipped for their form and properties, other cultures have added to the myths surrounding alliums. According to Pliny, garlic and onion were addressed as deities by the Egyptians at the taking of oaths.

Though many ancient cultures recognised the beneficial effects of garlic on curing a range of ailments, they were unable to understand why the cure happened — it was often attributed to magic or the supernatural. Illness was sometimes considered a manifestation of evil spirits or forces. Along with ceremonial magic, herbal remedies were linked to good spirits. Garlic was often the remedy of choice because it was frequently successful in healing. Equally, garlic was considered the ideal weapon to battle with dark forces.

HOLY MOLY

For centuries, garlic was believed to ward off demons, evil spirits and vampires. Homer, the 8th-century BC poet and author of the *Iliad* and the *Odyssey*, may have set the stage that elevated garlic's powers. During Odysseus's long journey, he set out to rescue his men who had been turned into pigs by the sorcery of the goddess, Circe. The god Hermes, aware that even the sword of a hero could not break the spell, gave a warning to Odysseus not to eat the Moly, a 'charmed herb' with a black root and a white flower, which was reputedly difficult for mortal men to dig up. This saved him from the same fate as his companions. Moly (*Allium moly*) is a wild, European plant of the lily family. Its other names are Golden Garlic and Lily Leek.

In his *Historia Planatarum*, written in about 230 BC, Theophrastus says that men digging for hellebore needed to protect themselves with garlic. Black hellebore was a poisonous plant, used by the Greeks for purging mania and by Melampus, a soothsayer and physician, around

1400 BC. He credited garlic with power to preserve the bearer of hellebore from sorcery, witchcraft, and possibly even from vampires. Wild garlic, or *Allium moly*, was employed as an antidote when poisonous plants such as hellebore and nightshade (mandrakes) were to be extracted.

GREEK MYTHOLOGY

Theophrastus relates how garlic was placed by the ancient Greeks on the piles of stones at crossroads as a supper for Hecate, goddess of crossroads and transitions in life. This became linked with the Greek custom used by travellers for protection from evil spirits. Placing an offering of garlic and other foods at crossroads was said to confuse demons and cause them to lose their way.

In 'The Superstitious Man', Theophrastus writes about superstition and the abject fear of the supernatural:

> The superstitious man typically tries to guard
> against pollution by constantly washing his hands
> and sprinkling himself from a sacred spring, and
> by chewing leaves of the sacred laurel; these
> precautions keep him busy the whole day. And
> should a cat chance to cross his path, he goes not
> a step further until he has tossed three stones
> across the road or until somebody else passes by.
> In the same way, seeing a harmless snake in the
> house makes him call on Sabazius Dionysus; and at
> the sight of the poisonous 'sacred snake' he
> hurries to have a shrine put up marking the spot;
> nor can he pass the ritual stones at a crossroads
> without pouring an offering from his oil-flask and
> kneeling to reverence them first . . . he is also
> likely to keep purifying his house all the time, on
> the excuse that Hecate has come to haunt it.
> Owls hooting while he is out for a walk upset
> him, too; he will not go on without first saying,
> 'Athena save us!' . . . Also, tombs and dead
> bodies and women in childbirth are bad omens
> that make him keep his distance . . . And in case
> he accidentally notices somebody making a meal
> out of Hecate's garlic at the crossroads, he feels

*compelled to bathe; and after that he calls in
priestesses to finish the purification by carrying
herbs or a poppy around him.*

CHILDBIRTH RITUALS
The passage about women in childbirth possibly explains
the custom in Greece of midwives preparing a birthing
room with garlic cloves, either hung up or crushed, to
keep evil spirits away. As the centuries passed, this
ancient custom became commonplace in many other
parts of Europe. In Greece, after delivering the baby, a
midwife would place a necklace with a clove of garlic
around the baby's neck.

Tales of the dead craving blood are found from the
earliest cultures. Vampire-like spirits called the Lilu are
mentioned in Babylonian demonology. These female
demons were said to roam during the hours of darkness,
hunting and killing newborn babies and pregnant women.
One of the demons, named Lilitu, was later adapted to
Jewish demonology as Lilith. Perhaps Theophrastus had
this in mind, too.

PLANT THE GARLIC
Because Roman generals believed that garlic gave their
armies courage, they planted fields of garlic in the
countries they conquered, in the belief that courage from
the battles fought would be transferred back to the
garlic.

NO GARLIC ALLOWED
Among the ancient Greeks, persons who partook of garlic
were not allowed to enter the temples of Cybele.
Similarly, Indian legends tell of battles between the devas
and the asuras, with garlic being a source of argument.
The Laws of Manu forbade eating garlic, leeks, onions and
mushrooms; they were considered to be unclean. Garlic
was forbidden from certain sacred places. Tibetan monks
were forbidden from entering monasteries if they had
eaten garlic.

HERBAL REMEDIES

Culpeper, the 17th-century physician I mentioned in Chapter 2, linked herbs with astrology. He associated garlic with the planet Mars, a fiery planet also connected with blood. Although he was popular at the time, this did nothing to aid his credibility with other scholars. Illness was often considered a manifestation of the evil spirits or supernatural forces. Along with ceremonial magic, herbal remedies were linked to good spirits. Garlic, with its antibiotic properties, was often the remedy of choice. Because it was frequently successful in healing, garlic was also considered the ideal weapon to battle the dark forces.

PROTECTOR FROM EVIL

Evidence can be found of garlics reputation as a protector from evil in nearly every continent. In the Prophet Muhammad's writings, he equates garlic with Satan, as he does when he describes the feet of the Devil as he was cast out of the Garden of Eden. Where his left foot touched the earth, garlic sprang up, while onion emerged from the footprint of his right foot. This story is told in Turkey as an ancient legend. In some societies an aversion to garlic was seen as evidence of being touched by evil, or even of being a vampire.

Some societies thought that garlic had a purification effect much like silver. People would hang it outside their doorways to keep evil spirits from entering their homes. Garlic was given out during church ceremonies, so that church officials could be sure that no evil spirits were attending.

The tradition is still kept in some parts of Greece to ward off demons and evil spirits in the same manner that incense does. Garlic can be worn in the clothes of an individual and, if you find garlic hanging in Greek businesses or houses, it is there for the purpose of warding off evil.

DREAMING OF GARLIC

Dreaming that there is garlic in the house is supposed to be lucky. Dreaming about eating garlic means you will discover hidden secrets.

PLAGUE CHARM

When plague ravaged Eastern Europe, people thought it was caused by evil spirits. They used onions and garlic as good luck charms to chase off the spirits. Even in the 17th century people hung strands of onions and garlic from their doorways and their windows, put it under their pillows and even hung it around their necks, to keep the vampires away. As recently as 1917—1918, Americans wore garlic garlands in public during an influenza outbreak.

SPECIAL POWERS

Henry IV was so keen on garlic as an aphrodisiac that apparently his 'breath could fell an ox at 20 paces'. Poor women — perhaps they were anaesthetised. Today, in some parts of the Middle East, a bridegroom wears a clove of garlic in his lapel to assure vitality on his wedding night.

FIDDLE-DE-DEE

Nero was said to eat leeks every day, in the belief that they would maintain the clarity of his voice.

RUNNING COACH

In some parts of Europe, there is a belief that, if a morsel of garlic is chewed by a man running a race, it will prevent his competitors from getting ahead of him. Perhaps it isn't chewing gum that modern athletes have in their mouths. Hungarian jockeys will sometimes fasten a clove of garlic to the bit of their horse. The belief is that any other contenders running close will fall back when they smell the offensive odour. As if!

POISON ANTIDOTE

Galen, a physician in Rome during the 2nd century AD, used garlic as an antidote to poisons. The Prophet Muhammad extolled its use for scorpion and snake bites.

VAMPIRES

The most famous of all garlic folklore is its association with vampires. This was popularised by Bram Stoker. The following passage describes how garlic is used to prepare a room to guard Lucy from the forces of evil:

*We went into the room, taking the [garlic] with
us. The Professor's actions were certainly odd and
not to be found in any pharmacopeia that I ever
heard of. First he fastened up the windows and
latched them securely. Next, taking a handful of
the flowers, he rubbed them all over the sashes,
as though to ensure that every whiff of air that
might get in would be laden with the garlic smell.
Then with the wisp he rubbed all over the jamb
of the door, above, below, and at each side, and
round the fireplace in the same way.*

*It all seemed grotesque to me, and presently I
said, 'Well, Professor, I know you always have a
reason for what you do, but this certainly puzzles
me. It is well we have no sceptic here, or he
would say that you were working some spell to
keep out an evil spirit.'*

*'Perhaps I am!' he answered quietly as he began
to make the wreath* which Lucy was to wear
round her neck.*

Dracula by Bram Stoker, (1897)

*This wreath was a necklace of garlic cloves.

Legend has made of Transylvania the home of the
vampires. Diseases caused by mosquito bites were
considered 'the touch of the vampire', and garlic came in
handy as a mosquito repellent, as described previously.
The reputation of garlic as a vampire repellent goes back
long before Stoker's relatively recent, gothic creation.
Many competing theories as to the origin of the vampire
story have to do with disease.

One theory tries to associate vampirism with rabies, but
this relies on the idea of rabies sufferers becoming
fixated on the smell of garlic. I don't think even garlic
would get through the effects of *la rage*, as the French
call rabies.

Apotropaics are objects intended to inhibit or ward off vampires and other evil supernatural creatures. These include garlic, sunlight, a branch of wild rose, the hawthorn plant, and all things sacred, for instance, holy water, a crucifix or a rosary. Different plants and objects function as apotropaics in other areas. Vampires were afraid of garlic and various other objects, depending on the tradition. Hawthorn was particularly valued as a suitable wood for making stakes. To ward off vampires, garlic could be worn, hung in windows or rubbed on chimneys and keyholes.

GARLIC FOR POPEYE?

The cartoon character Popeye's ancestor, Hercules, would sniff fresh bulbs of unpeeled garlic. Back in the 1930s Popeye's creator, Max Fleisher, was looking around for a special food to give the character special powers and strength. About ten years earlier a report based on the work of E. von Wolf, dating from 1870, had suggested that spinach was exceptionally rich in iron, calcium and vitamins A and C. The popularity of the cartoon character was responsible for a twentyfold increase in production. It's a pity that Fleisher didn't stick with garlic as the superfood, because, when a scientist looked again at spinach in 1937, someone discovered that a decimal point had been put in the wrong place, and that spinach only contained a tenth of the iron originally claimed. Most of the iron and calcium in spinach is bound to oxalic acid (not a nutrient) and can't be used by the human body, anyway. The garlic might well have been Popeye's source of superhuman strength, if not for the whiff!

KNOW YOUR ONIONS

This is going to sound a bit like a round of 'Call my Bluff'. Various accounts exist as to the origin of the phrase, which most people regard as meaning that someone is very well-informed about something. You can choose whichever interpretation you like best. Knowing your onions:

- was a term coined in the 1920s to indicate that the many varieties of onions that were cultivated over the years did not have standardised names from one region to another. Knowing your onions meant you

were familiar with those varieties that were grown and sold in the area where you lived.
- came from the name of the noted lexicographer and grammarian, C T Onions, who worked on the Oxford English Dictionary. Apparently, Onions was so well regarded that he became the epitome of the 'expert'.
- was first recorded in the magazine Harper's Bazaar, in March 1922. It was one of a set of phrases, concerned with being knowledgeable in a particular field. Others were to know one's oats, oil, apples and eggs.

GARLIC FESTIVALS

GILROY
Garlic festivals are celebrated in community events all across the world. One such festival, during the last weekend in July each year, is held in Gilroy, California. Self-styled as the 'garlic capital of the world', this might come as a surprise to a lot of people. The annual event attracts over 120,000 garlic lovers who gather to devour over 2 tons of garlic in every form, from appetisers, soups, salads, entrées and baked goods to the most surprising item, garlic ice cream.

The weekend event features music and entertainment, arts and crafts, special activities for children, a garlic cook-off and recipe contest. Amateur chefs compete for the top prize of $1,000 and a coveted crown of garlic. A beauty pageant sees the winners crowned Queen of Garlic or Belle of the Bulb.

FRENCH FESTIVALS
The French garlic capital is in Arleaux, north of Paris, in the area where some of the worst battles of World War I took place. There they produce over 200 million pounds of garlic a year. In the south of France, Le Grand Aioli is the event that celebrates the garlic harvest. Bowls of aioli, a sauce laced with garlic, are featured and the celebration attracts large crowds for a traditional meal of baby new potatoes, fresh vegetables, salt cod, and plenty of good French wine.

ISLE OF WIGHT

Not to be outdone, a community on the Isle of Wight has been successfully running Garlic Festivals for over 21 years and, having achieved their major fund-raising aims, the Newchurch Parish Sports and Community Association have decided not to hold any further Garlic Festivals. A sports pavilion, sports field, dual use community hall, recreation ground and numerous grants to parish organisations are testament to their success. The festivals were run to provide a value for money family fun day with entertainment. Happily for garlic lovers the festival has been taken over and still takes place in August, offering music, magic and some unusual garlic-flavoured food, according to their song for 2007, which also included garlic ice cream.

ROMANIA

If you're going to Eastern Europe, you might want to join the 120,000-plus people who attend the Romanian Garlic Festival in Copalau (near Botosani, in northern Romania) to get their garlic fix. Perhaps they are just playing safe, in case of vampires in the region . . .

Growing
Alliums

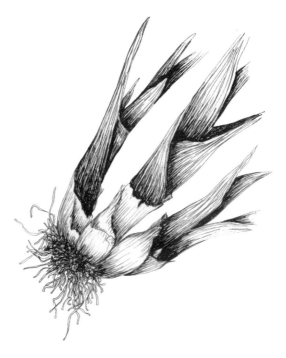

Most alliums are not really difficult to grow if you prepare the soil well before you start. Some are a bit more demanding than others but, essentially, getting the soil in good condition will guarantee at least some success. Alliums are susceptible to some pests, but they are not as hard to protect from common pests like slugs and snails, who probably don't like the taste. I've noticed my beetroot has done particularly well this year, planted up against the onions.

PREPARING THE SOIL
Grow main crops in full sun. If you have well-drained, light, friable loam, bully for you! Our garden in France is ideal for growing shallots, which don't seem to mind being neglected when we're not there to look after them. The same hasn't been true of our onions in England during dry spells, when they have suffered from the heavy clay they grow in. When rain stops, the soil dries out into a solid mass. The only answer is to add plenty of organic matter to fertilise the soil well before planting and to dig deeply. Double digging may be necessary, but that doesn't mean we always have the time or right weather for digging in the autumn in England. The best way is to start small and experiment with varieties of onions, leeks and shallots. I'm afraid I've given up on garlic and prefer to buy it, but my brother has produced some really good elephant garlic, down on his allotment in Devon. His onions are always bigger than mine too, but I don't bear a grudge, much . . .

ONIONS (ALLIUM CEPA)

One good thing about onions is that you can usually grow them in the same place, year after year, without any problems. Having dug deeply, the winter weather should have left the soil with only a light raking necessary, or so it says in some gardening books. Anyway, having dug out the crop of weeds that has taken root since you dug it and fed it with compost or manure in the autumn or winter, rake the soil to a fine tilth. Firm this down by walking over it in boots. Top dress if you want to, with a general fertiliser, like Growmore or organic chicken pellets, which don't smell like real chicken muck. If they are sown under cloche protection, main crop onions and sets can be sown four weeks earlier.

SEEDS OR SETS?

Which to choose? Seeds have certain advantages over sets, but need starting off earlier. This may be a problem if you live in a cold area (or if you have two gardens in different countries).

SEEDS:
- Are cheaper. You get a lot of seed for a couple of pounds: hundreds of them!
- Have more chance of failing due to bad weather.
- Need more attention.
- Are disease free.
- Give a greater choice and variety from many suppliers.

On the other hand, *SETS*:
- Are more expensive.
- Are more reliable.
- Are less work.
- Can be diseased before you plant them.
- Are restricted in choice by availability: you are dependent on suppliers' choices.

SOWING ONION SEEDS

You should be able to sow seeds from the middle of February until the end of March on dry, crumbly soil. If the weather is really wet, wait until the soil dries out a bit. Sow thinly in rows about 30 centimetres (12 inches) apart. As soon as you can, thin out the seedlings to about 5 centimetres (2 inches), then to about 10 centimetres (4 inches). You can use any thinnings as spring onions. Keep the weeds down by hoeing and water the seedlings in dry weather, but not when the bulbs are ripening. Seed onions will mature in about 24 weeks.

EARLY CROPS

If you are keen to steal a march on your friends and family, you might like to sow seeds in August and September in beds that were fertilised for previous crops. You can afford to plant more closely than in spring as some will inevitably be lost over the winter. In spring, the seedlings will start to grow faster and will be ready a good month before the main spring varieties.

ONION SETS
Prepare the soil as above, for seeds, in previously improved soil from another crop. Plant out in March to April, at 15 centimetres (6 inches) apart, with 30 centimetres (12 inches) between rows. Push the sets into the ground, leaving just the neck showing. Be prepared to push back any sets that pop out, or are dragged out by birds looking for nesting material. Sets often give better results in cold or wet areas than seeds and should be ready after about 20 weeks. If you are a beginner you might like to try heat-treated sets for ease and results without hassle.

HARVESTING ONIONS
Pull up salad onions whenever you need them. Other onions will be ready when the tops start to go yellow or brown and they may start to collapse. If not, bend the leaves down to allow more sun to dry the onions. As the foliage dries, lift the onions carefully and lay them out to dry in a row. If you can do this outside, so much the better, but if rain is likely, dry them in a shed, garage or greenhouse. Turn the bulbs daily. They make take a long time to dry, but it is important that you only store the sound, dry ones. They will keep well if stored in a dry, airy place, or braided in a rope if you want to show them off. Incidentally, don't store onions alongside potatoes as they will emit a gas that speeds up maturity, causing each to rot faster. There is a reason for storing onions on a rope as this enables the air to circulate around them, reducing the possibility of diseases and moulds.

SHALLOTS
SOWING
These can be planted out from February. Set the bulbs 24 centimetres (9 inches) apart, with about 35 centimetres (15 inches) between each row. Keep the weeds down with a hoe, but don't disturb the bulbs. As for onion sets, be prepared to re-set any bulbs that pop out. I protected our shallots from curious birds this year with netting.

HARVESTING SHALLOTS

Harvest as soon as the foliage starts to turn yellow, from mid-July onwards. Leave the whole clumps in the sun to dry for a few days, or take under cover if necessary. Turn the clumps daily. When they are completely dry, separate the bulbs and store in a cool, dry place. Save a few for planting out next year.

SALAD ONIONS

Spring onions or salad onions can be grown in soil previously manured for another crop. Sow the seeds thickly in shallow drills 1 centimetre (½ inch) deep. By making sowings in July/August and the following February, you may be able to keep fresh supplies from March until June. Alternatively, try sowing every three weeks or so from mid-March to early June to ensure a continuous supply.

Spring onions should be harvested when about 45 centimetres (18 inch) high and eaten within a day or so. They take about 11 weeks to mature.

ONIONS FOR PICKLING

Pickling onions can be sown in March or April on thin or poor soil. You won't need to thin them and they should be ready around July.

JAPANESE ONIONS

These are a relative newcomer to gardeners and allotment owners here in Britain. Japanese onions are treated in the same way as ordinary main crop onions for soil preparation, but the timing of planting is different. Sow the seeds in August outside and thin as necessary. They take about 45 weeks to mature, so will need to establish themselves before the winter sets in. When harvesting, treat, again, as main crop. They should be ready to harvest in May or June. They don't keep as long as main crop onions, so should be used fairly quickly.

EGYPTIAN ONIONS *(ALLIUM CEPA AGGREGATUM)*

These are something else! This clustering form of onion bears its bulbils on metre-high (3 foot) stems. They can be planted as sets, 24—30 centimetres (9—12 inches) apart in August or September. They will be ready the following year, from June. Once established, clumps can be divided and replanted in March. Funnily enough, they have nothing to do with Egypt, where they don't grow, but they have been discovered growing wild in North America.

WELSH ONIONS *(ALLIUM FISTULOSUM)*

These are non-bulbous perennials and look like multi-stemmed salad onions, sometimes called Everlasting Onions. They are hardy and the shoots are about the thickness of a pencil, growing together in clumps. They grow to about 30 centimetres (12 inches). The leaves can be used as chives and the shoots as salad onions. Propagate them by dividing clumps in March or April and setting bulbs about 24 centimetres (9 inches) apart. They don't need much attention, other than a replant and division each year.

Although called Welsh onions, they have little to do with Wales, where they weren't even introduced until 1629. *Allium fistulosum* is considered quite primitive in that it has never developed a bulb, but resembles a scallion with a slightly thickened stem. It has, however, gained fame as an important onion in oriental countries. Along with Egyptian Onions, they have given rise to hundreds of different cultivars and hybrids, particularly *Allium chinense*, the Chinese jiao tou and the Japanese rakkyo, pickling onions.

POTATO ONIONS

These onions form clusters of bulbils like shallots, just below the surface. They are mild in flavour and can be grown as shallots.

VARIETIES OF ONIONS

The following list is compiled from a variety of gardening sources and catalogues. It is by no means exhaustive, but aims to give an overview of what is available. You don't often see all of these in a garden centre and some are not grown in the UK.

Heirloom varieties are varieties that have been around for at least 50 years. They are not always the varieties that commercial growers use today, but those which have been growing in gardens and allotments for generations. If they didn't give such good results they would have disappeared, so they are worth a try in my book.

If you grow hybrids, don't save the seeds from any flowers. They won't give the expected results: more of a mongrel mixture than a pedigree.

GLOBE ONION VARIETIES

NAME	CHARACTERISTICS
Ailsa Craig	Heirloom, gold colour, good exhibitor, but not easy to grow.
Albion	Medium-sized white bulbs.
Autumn Queen	Non-bolting, large long lasting bulbs.
Bedfordshire Champion	Heirloom, excellent quality, yielding large globes with golden brown skin, good storage ability.
Bristol F1	Main crop variety with outstanding storage qualities and excellent skin colour. Produces uniform bulbs of high standard.
Brunswick	Beautiful, red-skinned, white flesh variety. Keeps well.
Buffalo	Good for an early harvest. Sow in summer for following year.
Burgundy	Large sweet variety.
Centurion	Grow from sets. Gold/straw colour, reliable in poor weather.
Copra	Yellow variety, long storage.
Derata De Parma	Organic, late maturing, golden globes, good storing.
F1 Forum	New, early cropper.
Giant Fen Globe	Old variety, heavy cropper with mild flavour.
Granex Hybrid	Similar to Vidalia onion. Bulbs are large and thick, and noted for their exceptionally sweet flavour. Produces high yields.
Granny Sweet	Heirloom, like Vidalia, very sweet, popular in USA.

Kamal	Red. Great taste and lovely colour.
Kelsae	Large, mild flavour but doesn't store so well.
Long De Florence Simiane (Long Red Florence)	Elongated, pinkish bulbs with a sweet flavour, good for eating raw.
Matador F1	From Rijnsburger stock, mild flavour.
New York Bold	Said to have lower water content, so caramelise faster. Can be safely stored for months.
Orion	Gold/straw colour. Available as heat-treated, good all rounder.
Red Baron	Popular in UK for deep red colour, good skins and thin necks.
Red Wethersfield	Large red sweet variety.
Reliance	Autumn maturing, non-bolting variety.
Rijnsburger	Popular as sets, solid, large brown-skinned, excellent keeper.
Rossa di Bassano	Has rings of white and rose, very good for salads.
Solidity	Autumn maturing, non-bolting variety.
Sturon	Organic. Yellowish bulbs of good quality and storage.
Stuttgarter Giant	Popular as sets, solid, brown-skinned, flattened bulbs, mild.
Sultans Onion	Mediterranean heirloom variety, bronze.
Sweet Spanish	Large, sweet variety.
Torpedo	Red Italian. Spindle-shaped bulbs, mild, but doesn't store well.
Utah Jumbo White	Large white bulbs, medium to late maturity. Good storage.
Vidalia	Sweet, large variety.
Walla Walla	Medium to very large and very sweet.
White Bermuda	Won't keep long.
White/Yellow Sweet Spanish	Popular in USA.
Yellow Ebenezer	Fair keeper, best choice for both green onions and all-purpose cooking.
Yellow Globe	Yellow variety. Long storage.

SALAD, BUNCHING AND JAPANESE-STYLE ONIONS

NAME	CHARACTERISTICS
Deep Purple	Salad onion, the only red bunching onion that keeps its colour at any temperature or age.
Electric	Japanese.
Evergreen Hardy White	Organic, bunching onion. Highly resistant to freezing and may be left in the ground year-round. Has resistance to pests and diseases.
Express Yellow	Japanese, gold/straw. Matures early summer.
Fukagawa	Heirloom, most popular with Japanese cooks. Very sweet.
Ishikura	Vigorous Japanese bunching onion with excellent flavoured, long slender white stalks and no bulbing.
Lisbon, White	Heirloom variety. Quick growing, clear white skins.
North Holland Blood Red Redmate	Mild flavour with crisp flesh when pulled young. If thinned out will produce larger, red-skinned bulbs.
Paris Silverskin	Excellent salad, cocktail or pickling onion, mature into small pickling onions.
Ramrod	Stiff-leaved variety, make successive sowings from spring onwards for summer, autumn and spring crops.
Red Beard	Salad onion. Vigorous, red stalks, crisp with mild flavour.
Savel	Salad onion with tall upright stem, can be sown at close density.
Sen Shui/ Senshyu	Japanese, yellow semi-globe, very reliable.
Summer Isle	Japanese bunching onion. Early maturing, sweet flavour, great for salads and stir fries.
Tough Ball	Japanese, matures end of June, can be used green from May.
White Portugal	Also used for pickling onions.
White Spear	Bunching onion.
Winter Over	Slightly larger bulbing than White Lisbon. Good winter hardiness, ideal for early or late cropping.

SHALLOTS

NAME	CHARACTERISTICS
Aristocrat	Strain of Hative de Niort.
Atlantic	Produces heavy yields which store well.
Creation	Highly resistant to bolting, stores well.
Dutch Red	Red skins with red/purple flesh, stores well.
Dutch Yellow	Small yellowy bulbs, prolific.
Giant Yellow	Consistently high yielding.
Golden Gourmet	Mild, reliable, high yielding.
Grise de Bagnolet	Grey shallot, popular in France, versatile.
Hative de Niort	Elongated, pear-shaped with dark brown skins.
Jermot	Coppery skins.
Pikant	Resistant to bolting, prolific.
Red Potato Onion	Hardy, bronze-red flesh, a good keeper.
Sante	Plant in Mid-April to prevent bolting. Pinkish white bulbs.
Topper	Mild, vigorous, golden yellow.

LEEKS *(ALLIUM PORRUM)*

Leeks can be grown where you have room from a previously harvested crop of potatoes, peas or salad crops. They need treating a little differently as they grow, because of their shape.

SOWING THE SEEDS
Sow seeds in March in drills, as for onions. At the end of June or during July lift the seedlings very carefully, avoiding damage to the roots. Trim the tops of the leaves to promote stronger root growth and plant out using either of the following methods:

LEVEL GROUND PLANTING
This method is best for short, thick stems and the least labour intensive, so the one I use. Prepare the ground as for onions and plant out about 15 centimetres (6 inches) apart for early to mid-season varieties or 24 centimetres

(9 inches) for later varieties. Allow about 35 centimetres (15 inches) between rows. Use a dibber to make 15 centimetres (6 inch) deep holes and drop the seedlings in. Water well to wash the soil from the sides of the hole over the roots.

TRENCH METHOD
This requires a trench 30 centimetres (12 inches) deep and wide, with 45 centimetres (18 inches) between rows for soil to be heaped on. Fill the bottom of the trench with well rotted manure and then plant the seedlings 2.5 centimetres (1 inch) deep and 24 centimetres (9 inches) apart in a single row. Tie cardboard collars round the stems and then pull some of the earth back into the trench. Repeat the earthing up every four weeks. When the collars are too small or if you want exhibits for a show, use bigger structures, such as drainpipes to protect the stems and foliage from grit. Fill the insides of the pipes with wood shavings or wool for a protective packing.

VARIETIES OF LEEKS
I was amazed by the number of varieties of leeks there are. You certainly don't find all of these easily. Here is a small sample to try.

NAME	CHARACTERISTICS
American Flag	Tall, thick stem, mild onion flavour, very dependable.
Albana Autumn Giant	Medium-length shaft, minimal bulbing.
Bulgarian Giant	Fine, thin autumn variety.
Carentan	Organic, large thick stems with blue-green foliage for cropping October to early January.
Farinto	Late autumn, winter, frost hardy, medium to long shafts.
Giant Winter 3	Late, thick, very hardy, producing in spring.
Hannibal	Long, blanched, autumn variety.
Jolant	Vigorous, mild, early cropper, good for mini leeks.
King Richard	Long straight stems, autumn and winter use.

Lyon Prizetaker	Solid stems of good size, good general use.
Musselburgh	Heirloom, medium long, thick blanching, very popular in northern areas.
Oarsman	Medium white shanks of good size, dark green foliage, very little wastage.
Prenora	Very vigorous, medium early variety for lifting in autumn. Blue-green foliage, white medium thickness.
Rami	Early summer cropping, medium green, robust leaves, medium long shafts.
St Victor	French variety, extremely hardy.
Splendid (Gennevilliers Sel)	Long stemmed early variety.
Tadorno	Medium length, very upright, extremely hardy, crops December to March.
Varna	Best for mini-leeks, ready late.
Walton Mammoth Tornado	Very high yielding, good cold tolerance, November–March harvesting. Suitable for baby leeks.
Yates Empire	Uniform, dark green, late variety.

GARLIC *(ALLIUM SATIVUM)*

I have to hold my hands up here and say that I have never successfully grown garlic, even though we get through loads of it in the kitchen. Garlic grows best in light, well-manured soil which has been dug during the winter. It likes a sunny position that is not too dry. These requirements have always defeated my meagre attempts at cultivation. Given that there are so many other things that do grow under the conditions we have, I'm quite content to buy the garlic.

The theory of growing garlic is as follow:

- Buy reliable bulbs. If ordering from specialist suppliers, get in early, as stocks seem to sell out quickly. You can buy bulbs from the supermarket, but don't think that you can get away with using up a dried up old bulb you found at the back of the kitchen cupboard. Separate the cloves out just before you plant them so that the root nodules don't dry out.

- Plant in October in mild areas, or February elsewhere, as separate cloves, in drills about 5 centimetres (2 inches) deep and set about 15 centimetres (6 inches) apart, with 30—40 centimetres (12—15 inches) apart.
- Remove any flowers (scapes) that form as soon as possible, so that the nutrients are used to develop the bulbs.
- Harvest when the foliage turns yellow. Lift carefully so that you don't nip any of the cloves and release the allicin or oil. Dry thoroughly, as for onions. Store in a dry, airy, frost-free place.

Garlic is at its best when fresh, known as wet garlic. It is less pungent than when dry and also sweeter. Garlic seems to be a lot harder to get hold of than onion sets or seeds, although I was surprised to find so many varieties that are available. They fall into two main categories, although there are other, similar plants of the garlic type also available.

SOFTNECK OR COMMON GARLIC
Softneck garlic is the most commonly found supermarket garlic. This is because it is easier to grow and plant mechanically and also keeps for longer than hardneck varieties. Softnecks have white papery skin and an abundance of white or blushed pink cloves, often forming several layers around the central core. A flexible stalk allows softneck garlic to be formed into garlic braids or plaits quite easily, like onions. The two main types are silverskin and artichoke:

- Silverskin garlic is the easiest to grow, apparently, and keeps longer.
- Artichoke garlic tends to have fewer, but larger cloves and a milder flavour. The outer layers are coarser and sometimes have purple blotches.

HARDNECK VARIETIES
Hardneck garlic is technically known as the *ophioscorodon* variety. It has been suggested that the name originates from the Greek *ophis* meaning snake. Hardneck garlics have a stalk, which coils from the top. On the top of this stalk, or scape, grow a number of bulbils, often referred

to as garlic flowers. These varieties of garlic have fewer, larger cloves then the softnecks and less of an outer bulb wrapper, sometimes none at all. This reduces their shelf-life, which is probably why you don't see it so often in the supermarket. Varieties include rocambole, porcelain and purple stripe.

- Rocambole garlic has up to a dozen cloves of a tan or brown colour.
- Porcelain garlic has a satiny white exterior and as few as four cloves. It is often mistaken for elephant garlic (see below).
- Purple stripe garlic is highly distinctive because of its colouring and is popular on our local market in the south-west of France.

Rocambole is by far the most distinctive of hardneck varieties. It is unlike common garlic because it throws up a flowering stem, or scape. The bulb has relatively little outer skin, making it very easy to peel and use, but having the downside of suffering from rough handling in storage. The bulbs don't look as attractive as bulbs of common garlic. There is only one ring of decent-sized cloves arranged around the woody central flower stalk, so there are no small, inner bits that are too small to crush. It keeps almost as well as common garlic if stored carefully. The tall flowering scapes make a twisting loop as it unfurls to reveal not flowers, but tiny little bulbils. This is where it gets the alternative name, 'serpent garlic' from. Clipping the flower stalk off early on, significantly improves bulb size, although the scapes are edible and considered a gourmet's delight by some people. Rocambole needs a cool winter and spring, and will not succeed in hot areas. I'll have to give it a try!

OTHER TYPES OF GARLIC

ELEPHANT GARLIC *ALLIUM AMPELOPRASUM*
This plant belongs to a family whose ancestors incude the wild leek, and the species has survived in many forms. One of them is the elephant garlic. It has enormous cloves but little garlic flavour, tasting more like a leek.

Many people are attracted to elephant garlic simply because of its size, assuming that it must be more strongly flavoured than ordinary garlic, but they are in for a big disappointment. The bulbs can weigh over 450 grams (1 pound): in fact, a single clove of elephant garlic can be as large as a whole bulb of ordinary garlic. Elephant garlic is to garlic what leeks are to onions: less intense and sweeter. When buying elephant garlic, follow the same guidelines as for ordinary garlic: look for heads that are firm with plenty of dry, papery covering. It is more perishable than ordinary garlic so it doesn't keep as long, but can be used where a subtle hint of garlic is wanted without overpowering the rest of the food.

CHINESE GARLIC STEMS, SUAN TAI
Chinese garlic has a symmetrical bulb in thin purple or silver skin, but has little flavour. Its stems are greens about 30 centimetres (12 inches) long and not hollow like green onions, but solid and about the width of a pencil. When cut, the escaping aroma is obviously one of garlic. In China, garlic flower stems are a side product of the garlic bulb. The bulbs are cultivated in the usual way, but the flower stems are cut in early summer when they are green, and harvested very carefully so that the bulb will not be damaged and can be left to mature. The stems, sold in bundles, are too strong to use raw, but can be an excellent addition to dishes requiring just a hint of garlic.

GARLIC CHIVE, CHINESE CHIVE
Garlic chives do not taste, look or cook like common chives. They come in three forms. One is a green leafy form, another is a blanched yellow form and the third has buds on the end of the stems. They smell of garlic, not chives. The plant has been cultivated for centuries in China, Japan and parts of eastern Asia. They can be stir-fried, steamed whole or simmered in broth.

RAMSONS OR BEAR'S GARLIC *(ALLIUM URSINUM)*
Ramsons garlic is wild garlic once cultivated in northern and central Europe as a vegetable, medicinal plant and herb. It is now found throughout Europe and in Asia. The spiky leaves have a strong garlic aroma and taste because of their allicin content. In northern Europe, it grows wild

in damp deciduous forests and in shady, moist locations, as well as in gardens. I remember being surprised by the smell of it when I was a child and we visited a local park with a wild bit of woodland attached. It was nothing like any other plant smell. The leaves are picked before the plant flowers in May and can be chopped to add to salads and other vegetable dishes.

GARLIC VARIETIES AVAILABLE IN THE UK
I've tracked down the following varieties as available to grow in the UK, although many are out of stock before the season has even begun. A surprisingly large number of them come from the Isle of Wight: so that's why they have garlic festivals there!

NAME	CHARACTERISTICS
Albi	Pink variety from France.
Albigensian Wight	From SW France, large softneck, ancient variety.
Arno	Large white/pink, non-flowering.
California Late	Spicy, hot flavour.
Chesnok Wight	From the Ukraine, rocamboles can be stir-fried.
Cristo	Medium, well suited to UK. 25 cloves, strong, hot.
Early Purple	Very large, violet hardneck, early variety.
Early Wight	Very early bulbs, May onwards, eat wet or green.
Freudenberger	Austrian, good in N Europe, medium size.
German Red	Vigorous, spicy flavour.
Germidour	French, good in UK gardens, 12—16 cloves, mild in a cool climate.
Iberian Wight	Spanish softneck, grows well in UK, big cloves.
Jolimont	New, large variety, recommended.
Lautrec Wight	From SW France, white skinned, purple cloves.
Mako	Hungarian, hot strong flavour.
Mediterranean Wight	From S France, grows well in UK, good for wet or green garlic.
Music	Hardneck, well suited to cooler climates, 5—6 cloves.
Moraluz	Hardneck purple stripe, very large, very hot.

Oswego White	Softneck, very large bulbs, good for roasting.
Pink Lady	Light pink clove, long dormant period.
Printanor	Grow in autumn or spring. Good storage.
Purple Wight	Early cropper, best eaten wet, nutty flavour.
Red Janice	Solid stripes, from Rep Georgia, hot, brown cloves.
Solent Wight	French, well adapted to UK, milder than Mako.
Spanish Roja	Old hardneck variety, strong flavour.
Sprint	Earliest cropper. Cut flowers off.
Sultop	White heads with red cloves.
Thermidrome	French, commercial bulb, large with good flavour.
Venetian/Italian White	Comes from the Po valley, dense white bulb, keeps well.
High Vigour White Pearl	Grow from October for early crops.

OTHER GARLIC VARIETIES

Most of these varieties are from the USA, where California now has a thriving garlic industry. Although they are not all available for growing, I loved some of the names and felt I had to include them.

PORCELAIN GARLICS
    Dan's Russian
    Fish Lake 3
    Georgian Fire
    German Stiffneck
    German White
    Italian Porcelain
    Leningrad
    Music
    Northern Quebec
    Northern White
    Polish Hardneck
    Polish Jenn
    Red Rezan
    Romanian Red

Rosewood
Susan Delafield
Ukrainian Mavniv
Weingarten
Wild Buff
Yugoslavian Porcelain
Zemo

PURPLE STRIPE GARLICS
Bogatyr
Brown Tempest
Chesnok Red
Duganskij
Khabar
Metechi
Persian Star
Purple Glazer
Siberian

ROCAMBOLE GARLICS
Baba Franchuk's
Carpathian
Colorado Black
Dan's Italian
Dominics
French Red
German Red
Israeli
Killarney Red
Korean Purple
Legacy
Marino
Mountain Top
Purple Max
Puslinch
Roja
Spanish Roja
Yerina
Yugoslavian

ARTICHOKE GARLICS
   Asian Tempest
   California Early
   California Late
   Chinese Purple
   Early Red Italian
   Inchelium Red
   Japanese
   Korean Purple
   Lorz Italian
   Purple Cauldron
   Red Toch
   Simoneti
   Susanville
   Thermidrome

SOFTNECK / SILVERSKIN
   Locati
   Mexican Red Silver
   Mid French
   Nootka Rose
   Rose du Var
   Russian Softneck
   Sicilian Gold
   Sicilian Silver
   Silver Rose
   Silverwhite
   Sweet Haven
   Thai
   Tibetan
   Western Rose
   Wildfire

CHIVES (ALLIUM SCHOENOPRASUM)

Chives are hardy perennials which are easy to grow and increase rapidly in size, given the right conditions. They like loamy soil and full sun or part shade, but do well in containers by the back door, where, left to flower, they will give a good show. The leaves give a mild oniony flavour and are used in salads, egg or cheese dishes and soups. They need frequent watering in dry weather.

CARE OF CHIVES

Plants die down in winter and disappear until spring. New leaves will appear and be ready to cut by early May. Top dress the plants in March or April. To divide a clump, wait until September or October. Use a sharp knife to cut into smaller bunches. Replant about 30 centimetres (12 inches apart). You'll need to do this about every four years to prevent the clumps getting too big. You could pot one lot up for indoor use, over the winter, when there isn't much fresh greenery around for garnishing.

Chives can also be grown from seed in March, outdoors in drills. Thin the seedlings to about 15 centimetres (6 inches) and transplant to their new permanent home in May. Remove dead flower heads to help the leaves grow better.

To 'harvest', cut the leaves close to the ground and use fresh. They can be frozen, but you don't really need to if you keep a pot indoors for winter use.

ONION PESTS AND DISEASES

There are a few nasties to watch out for when dealing with alliums, but there are ways of preventing some problems. If you handle the young seedlings carefully and don't break roots or stems, then you're doing well at deterring pests such as onion fly.

Another way to deter pests is to plant things they don't like nearby. Companion planting is a solution you might like to try, for example planting parsley near to alliums, which is said to keep onion flies away. It certainly worked for me this year.

A further advantage of growing onions can be to keep carrot flies off your developing carrots, although, having clay to grow on, I don't bother with carrots. I read somewhere recently that chives can deter moles and that chopped chives can keep moths way. There's something to try!

To keep the soil free from disease, be careful about removing any dead plants or leaves. Don't put diseased leaves or plants into compost bins, or the spores will spread. If your plants suffer from any of the diseases described, give the soil a rest and grow the plants somewhere else for a few years. Most problems mean that destroying the plant is the best solution.

PESTS
ONION FLY
The onion fly maggot attacks roots of onions and leeks. The fly looks like a normal fly and lays eggs in spring on the neck of the allium. The developing larvae will tunnel into the onion and destroy it. Hoe around the plants regularly to expose the eggs. The time of greatest risk is when you thin the onions, as the flies are attracted by the scent. Growing from onion sets removes the need for thinning and then the onions are unlikely to be attacked. If attacked, the plants will wilt at the base and you will see tunnels in the plant tissue.

EELWORM

Eelworms are microscopic worms in the soil which invade the leaves and bulbs and lead to swelling and distortion. There is really no effective chemical cure, and it will be necessary to stop growing onions in the patch of ground for three to four years.

DISEASES

WHITE ROT

This can affect onions, leeks and garlic. The leaves go yellow, and white or grey fluffy fungus appears at the base of the plant. The root and base of the bulb rot away.

DOWNY MILDEW

Leaves go grey and fall over. In wet weather they go black. Fungal threads spread deep into the plant tissue.

ONION SMUT

Lead-coloured, swollen blisters release black, powdery spores. Diseased plants will continue to grow, but the spores are produced annually and will spread to new, healthy plants.

SOFT ROT

This affects stored onions and leeks, when they can become slimy, soft and stinky.

RUST

This is most troublesome if there is a potassium deficiency in the soil. Leeks and chives may suffer from orange, powdery spots on older leaves.

Cooking With Alliums

Cooking and Eating Alliums

Onions can even make heirs and widows weep.
Benjamin Franklin

Everyone has likes and dislikes when it comes to vegetables, but I haven't come across many people who don't like onions: they just don't like peeling them. I didn't like leeks when I was younger, but have since realised that this was to do with the preparation or cooking rather than the flavour. If you're not careful with leeks, they can be very stringy and stick in your throat. The same is not so true of garlic, which is not to everyone's taste. In the Middle Ages cooking was awash with onions and Richard II is said to have eaten an elaborate salad of garlic, onions and a whole heap of herbs, but the 19th-century poet, Shelley, was not too impressed when he visited Paris, where he was shocked to see ladies of rank eating garlic. How dare they!

Onion sellers visiting the south of England during the 1930s promoted French onions in Britain and also helped to further the myth that the French only eat onions and garlic, as well, of course, as other unmentionable delicacies like snails and frogs. What nonsense! It was Elizabeth David who gave garlic some respectability when she promoted her Provençal dishes and Mediterranean diet.

WHO EATS ONIONS?
Annual worldwide production of onions is said to be 6.7 million acres, producing 105 billion pounds. Main producers are China, India, the USA, Turkey and Pakistan. The record for annual consumption of onions goes to Libya, where average consumption is 30.4 kilograms (67 pounds) per year. Given this extraordinary fact, I thought I'd look at some other countries and their onion consumption. Apparently, world consumption works out at 6.2 kilograms (13.7 pounds) per person. That means that Libya must eat an awful lot of onions, especially when you consider cultures where onions are not eaten. The EU

average seems to be about the same as the UK average consumption, of 5 kilograms (11 pounds) per year, per head, which breaks down to 98 grams per week. My family must be eating several other people's onions as well as our own! Not all EU countries seem to give specific figures for onions, but the Czech Republic weighs in at an impressive 9.9 kilograms (21.8 pounds) per annum, although consumption is falling, as it is in Poland. Despite the health study showing that adults in the Netherlands gain benefits from eating onions, they only consume 4.4 kilograms (9.7 pounds).

Americans eat 8.5 kilograms (18.8 pounds) of fresh onions on average each year, which is, apparently, a 50% increase on 20 years ago. It must be because of all the burgers and onion rings consumed. The USA is now a major producer of sweet, mild onions, and at least two states, Georgia and Texas, have onions as their official state vegetable!

PRODUCERS OF GARLIC

The main garlicproducing country in the world is China, which has recently increased its share to 75% of the garlic produced. Most is produced in the Shandong Province, south-east of Beijing. South Korea and India come in second and third with 5% each. The USA ranks fourth with 3% of the world's production. Garlic production in China tripled during the 1990s. In the USA, California produces 84% of the domestic fresh and dehydrated product market. Four other states produce reasonable harvests: Nevada, Oregon, Washington and New York. Sadly, dehydrated garlic accounts for roughly 75% of US consumption.

SELECTING ALLIUMS TO EAT

Garlic freshly harvested does not have the same pungency and you may not even recognise it as that zesty, bracing herb you've always known. But give it time to dry and 'cure' for about a month, and you'll be sharing that old familiar garlic breath with anyone who stands within three feet of you. Here are some pointers:

- For maximum flavour and nutritional benefits, always purchase fresh garlic. Garlic in flake, powder or paste form may be more convenient and less smelly, but you won't get the same health benefits from these forms.
- Always buy garlic that is plump and has unbroken skin. Don't buy damp, squashy garlic. I'm not saying you should go round squeezing it, but have a little feel if you can. Avoid garlic that has begun to sprout. This may cause inferior flavour and texture.
- Size is not an indication of quality. If your recipe calls for a large amount of garlic, remember that it is always easier to peel and chop a few larger cloves.
- Fresh garlic is available throughout the year. Store fresh garlic in a cool, dark place away from exposure to heat and sunlight. This will help maintain its maximum freshness and help prevent sprouting. You don't need to keep it in the fridge. Some people freeze peeled garlic but this reduces flavour and changes its texture.
- Whole garlic bulbs should keep fresh from two weeks to two months. Remove any cloves that appear to be dried out or mouldy. Once you break the head of garlic, the shelf-life is greatly reduced.
- Don't keep garlic in oil unless refrigerated, as explained previously, for health reasons.

ONIONS

Store your onions in a cool, dry, ventilated place: not in the refrigerator. Always remove from plastic bags as soon as possible, as lack of air movement reduces storage life. Chopped or sliced onions can be stored in a sealed container in your refrigerator for up to seven days.

SOME CLASSIC DISHES
FROM AROUND THE WORLD

A classic dish in Turkey and Greece is Skordalia. This is a combination of mashed potatoes, heads of roasted garlic, bread and olive oil. Another, similar version in Romania is Mujdei, which is made by blending bread, garlic and olive oil together. In Azerbaijan whole bulbs of garlic are pickled in red wine vinegar. These are served with a combination of cucumber pickles, fresh tomatoes and watercress. Pickled garlic has different beneficial compounds and eating pickled garlic does not give rise to garlic breath or sweating garlic hours later. The acid in vinegar neutralises the alliin and slowly breaks down the cloves into odourless, water-soluble compounds. Pickled garlic, called Kratiem Dong, is popular in Thailand, while in Laos, Sousi Pa, a dish of fish and coconut sauce, includes five cloves of garlic per serving. In the Balkans whole heads of garlic are pickled and then roasted. Finally, the garlic is puréed and seasoned with salt and olive oil.

Curry, the mixture of spices that seasons Indian cuisine, often includes large quantities of garlic. Fresh ginger, garlic and onions are the three main seasonings that arrived with the early Moghuls, the Muslims who came from Turkey and Iran and settled in northern India.

With the exception of Buddhists, the Chinese consider garlic and onions as necessities in their diet. Being the world's largest producer, this is obviously a good thing. Many traditional dishes feature a garlic sauce made with at least two heads of garlic, sautéed with peanut oil, sherry, rice vinegar, soy sauce, and black bean chilli sauce. Koreans enjoy Kimchee, for which garlic provides the characteristic flavour. Garlic shoots are edible and offer a distinct flavour of garlic, though much milder. Asian cooks include them in stir-fries or in salads.

Throughout the Middle East hummous, a chickpea or bean-based appetiser prepared with fresh minced garlic, is a daily staple. It makes an appearance in our house on an almost daily basis, too!

In Eastern Europe many people like preparing and eating garlic pickles. In Spain several cloves are chopped and added to Romesco sauce, and Moroccans include garlic in their spicy harissa sauce. This is an experience to be treated with respect. If offered harissa with tagine or couscous, my advice is to ask for it to be served separately, or at least on only part of the couscous. I've seen grown men in extreme discomfort from trying to impress their companions. Eating a sugar cube is the answer, if in distress.

Although the Americans have never fully embraced garlic, there is apparently a restaurant where every dish is prepared with as many cloves of garlic as the customer desires: even ice cream!

In Chinese cuisine, young bulbs of garlic are pickled for 3–6 weeks in a mixture of sugar, salt and spices. The shoots are often pickled in Russia and eaten as an appetiser. Immature scapes (flower stems, if you missed the gardening chapter) are tender. They are also known as 'garlic spears'. Scapes generally have a milder taste than garlic cloves. They are often prepared like asparagus. Garlic leaves are a popular vegetable in many parts of Asia.

I hope you enjoy at least some of the recipes in the following sections. Please remember that metric measures are only roughly equivalent to imperial ones, so for best results, don't mix the two measures in the same recipe.

Soups, Sauces & Salad Dressings

SOUPS

ROASTED GARLIC AND CAULIFLOWER SOUP

You can prepare the roasted garlic the day before, while the oven is hot, to save fuel.

You will need:
1 large head (whole bulb) garlic
3 teaspoons olive oil
2 medium leeks white part only, washed and shredded
1 teaspoon dried thyme
Salt
¼ teaspoon white pepper
450 g (1 lb) coarsely chopped fresh cauliflower
850 ml (30 fluid oz) chicken stock
4 tablespoons freshly grated Parmesan cheese
2 tablespoons crème fraiche

Method:
1. Preheat the oven to 200°C (400°F, gas mark 6).
2. Remove the paper layer from the garlic but do not peel or separate the cloves. Cut off the top of the bulb, place it on a sheet of foil and drizzle ½ teaspoon of oil over the top. Roast for about 40 minutes, or until the cloves are soft.
3. Cool the garlic and then squeeze it from the skins directly into a small bowl. Mash with a fork and set aside.
4. In a large saucepan, heat the rest of the oil over a medium heat. Add the leeks, thyme, salt and white pepper. Stir for about 5 minutes, until the leeks are translucent, but not browned. Stir in the roasted garlic and add the cauliflower and stock.
5. Bring to the boil, reduce the heat to medium-low and cook for 8–10 minutes, or until the cauliflower is tender. Cool for 10 minutes or so.
6. Using a food processor, purée the soup, leaving a few leeks and the odd piece of cauliflower for added texture.
7. Reheat the soup and serve in bowls with a swirl of crème fraiche and some Parmesan cheese.

FRENCH ONION SOUP

This is a hearty lunchtime dish for cold winter weather. The bread and cheese topping is a great contrast to the hot soup and as the soup soaks into the toasted bread, you get a really filling, satisfying dish. Serve with forks and spoons.

You will need: **Serves 4**
    80 g (3 oz) butter or margarine
    1 kg (2 lb) onions, very finely sliced into rings
    150 ml (5 fluid oz) white wine
    600 ml (1 pt) strong beef stock
    2 cloves garlic, crushed

For the cheesy bread topping:
    2-day-old baguette
    Emmental cheese, grated

Method:
1. Place the butter and all of the onions and the garlic in a large pan over a medium heat. Cook the onion rings until they caramelise, stirring occasionally. This may take a while.
2. Add the white wine and simmer until it has almost evaporated.
3. Add the beef stock and simmer for half an hour.
4. Meanwhile, cut thick slices of baguette and place under the grill until just brown on both sides. Remove from the grill and top with grated cheese. Return to the grill until the cheese has melted.
5. Serve the soup and place the grilled bread and cheese on top. Delicious!

VICHYSSOISE

This recipe has been claimed by both France and USA as their own. It is a chilled version of leek and potato soup. Apparently the soup is derived from the hot version being cooled down with milk in warm weather. I think I prefer my soup hot, in cold weather.

You will need: Serves 4

50 g (2 oz) butter
1 medium onion, chopped
300 g (10 oz) leeks, finely sliced
Splash of white wine (optional)
110 g (4 oz) potatoes, peeled and sliced
285 ml (10 fluid oz) vegetable stock
salt and freshly ground black pepper
285 ml (10 fluid oz) milk
2 tablespoons cream or crème fraiche
1 tablespoon snipped chives
1 tablespoon chopped parsley
Salt and pepper

Method:

1. Gently sweat the chopped leeks and the chopped onion in butter until soft, but don't let them brown.
2. Add the potatoes, wine and stock to the pan, with salt and pepper to taste. Again, do not overcook them. Bring to the boil, and simmer very gently for 30 minutes.
3. Blend in a food processor until very smooth and allow to cool thoroughly. Add the milk.
4. To serve, chilled, pour into bowls and garnish with the cream or crème fraiche and herbs.

LEEK AND POTATO SOUP

This version is best served without blending. Make sure the leeks are prepared by slicing each leek longwise twice and then chopping from top to bottom. This prevents stringy bits of leek catching in your throat, which can be off-putting!

You will need: Serves 4

2 tablespoons butter or margarine
1 clove grated garlic
450 g (1 lb) leeks (roughly two large ones)
450 g (1 lb) potatoes
900 ml (2 pints) chicken stock
Pinch of salt
¼ teaspoon pepper
285 ml (10 fluid oz) milk

Method:
1. Clean and chop the leeks carefully, as above.
2. Melt the butter or margarine in a pan and add the chopped leeks and garlic. Fry over a low to medium heat until the leeks are soft but not browned.
3. Peel and chop the potatoes into cubes. Add all the remaining ingredients except the milk.
4. Bring to the boil and then let it simmer for about 30 minutes.
5. Just before serving, add the milk to the soup, heat and stir well.

MEXICAN GARLIC SOUP

One version of this soup I found suggests that it is perfect for protecting you from stomach troubles, mosquitoes and unwanted company! What more could you ask for in a soup? The parsley should help with the garlic breath.
If you don't want the poached eggs you could serve with toasted bread, as for the onion soup recipe above, and sprinkle the cheese on the bread. Traditionally, a raw egg is served in each bowl, but that isn't a very good idea on safety grounds.

You will need: Serves 4–6
    10 cloves garlic
    Salt and cayenne pepper
    1 teaspoon flour
    4 eggs
    2 tablespoons butter
    2 tablespoons grated Emmental cheese
    1 litre (2 pints) beef or chicken stock
    2 tablespoons chopped parsley

Method:
1. Sauté the whole, peeled cloves of garlic over a low heat until tender. The garlic should be cooked but not brown. Remove from the pan.
2. Mash the garlic as fine as possible and stir in the flour. Return to the pan.
3. Add the stock, boil and simmer for 15 minutes.
4. Add seasonings. Break the eggs gently into the soup so

that the yolk doesn't break. When the eggs are poached, serve in bowls with parsley and cheese on top.

BROCCOLI AND LEEK SOUP

Don't be put off by the colour of this soup. It beats pea soup any day!

You will need: Serves 4—6

    225 g (8 oz) broccoli florets
    1 medium onion, chopped
    2 medium leeks
    500 ml (1 pint) stock: chicken or vegetable
    100 g (4 oz) low fat soft cheese
    225 ml (8 fluid oz) milk
    Salt and pepper
    25 g (1 oz) butter or margarine
    1 tablespoon flour

Method:
1. Trim the broccoli into minute florets and the smaller stalks finely. Clean and shred the leeks, as described above (Leek and Potato Soup).
2. Melt the butter or margarine and cook the leeks, onion and broccoli stalks until soft but not brown.
3. Stir in the flour to thicken and gradually add the milk, seasoning and the stock. Simmer for about 15 minutes and then allow to cool slightly.
4. Steam the broccoli for about 3 minutes and drain.
5. Blend the soup with the soft cheese until smooth. Return to the pan and add the broccoli florets, reheating to serve.

SAUCES

BREAD AND ONION SAUCE

This is far too good just to have with roast turkey at Christmas. I like it with roast chicken any time of the year. It also helps to make dry chicken more palatable. You can do most of the preparation well before, especially infusing the milk with the onion and cloves, and finish off when making the gravy.

You will need: Serves 4
  1 medium onion
  10 whole cloves
  Black pepper, freshly ground
  225 ml (8 fluid oz) milk
  50 g (2 oz) breadcrumbs
  1 tablespoon double cream or crème fraiche
  Bay leaf

Method:
1. Cut the onion in half and stick the cloves in.
2. Put the onion and bayleaf into a saucepan with the milk and slowly bring to the boil. Remove from the heat, put a lid on the saucepan and leave aside for at least an hour.
3. Remove the onion and spices, add the breadcrumbs and leave on a low heat until the bread swells up and thickens the sauce.
4. Just before serving, check seasoning, reheat if necessary and stir in the cream or crème fraiche.

SAGE AND ONION SAUCE

This is a good accompaniment for roast game, pork or just sausages.

You will need:
  670 g (1.5 lb) onions, sliced
  2 tablespoons vegetable oil
  100 g (4 oz) carrots, thinly sliced
  285 ml (10 fluid oz) chicken or vegetable stock

1½ tablespoons fresh sage, chopped

1 teaspoon lemon juice

Salt and pepper

2 tablespoons low fat crème fraiche

Method:

1. Fry the onions in the oil in a frying pan with a lid for about 5 minutes. Add the carrots and cook for another couple of minutes.

2. Pour in the stock, add the seasoning and most of the sage. Cover and simmer for about 15 minutes and then cool.

3. Blend the sauce and add the rest of the sage.

4. Reheat, adjust the seasoning and add the lemon juice. Stir in the crème fraiche, and serve.

GARLIC AND HERB SAUCE

This is a good accompaniment to grilled meat or barbecued food. Prepare in advance so that the herbs can get to work on the yoghurt. If you are more adventurous, try making your own mayonnaise in the next recipe, but for speed and results, this one is pretty good.

You will need:

1 large clove garlic

150 ml (5 fluid oz) low fat natural yoghurt

2 tablespoons chopped parsley

2 tablespoons chopped chives

Pinch of salt

Black pepper

Method:

1. Crush the garlic to a paste with the salt and add to the yoghurt.

2. Add plenty of pepper and the chopped herbs. Stir well to combine and then leave aside until required.

AIOLI

This is the traditional garlic mayonnaise. It helps to have a food processor, but you can make do without.

You will need:
- 4 garlic cloves, peeled, chopped fine
- 2 egg yolks
- ⅛ teaspoon sea salt
- 225 ml (8 fluid oz) olive oil
- 1 teaspoon Dijon mustard
- ½ teaspoon cold water
- 1 teaspoon lemon juice

Method:
1. Purée, mash or blend the garlic as finely as possible and add to the olive oil.
2. Place the egg yolks and mustard in a medium mixing bowl and whisk together for 2 minutes, or until smooth. While still whisking, begin to drizzle in half the oil in a thin, slow stream. This must be done very slowly or the oil will not emulsify and your sauce will not thicken.
3. When about half the oil is in, and the mixture is beginning to resemble mayonnaise, add the water, lemon juice, salt and pepper.
4. Whisk together, then continue to drizzle in the oil while whisking.
5. The mixture should be thick, creamy and not too garlicky. If it gets too thick, add a little more water, warmed slightly.

SALAD DRESSINGS

BASIC DRESSING RECIPE

You will need:
>   60–90 ml (4–6 tablespoons) olive oil
>   1 tablespoon cider, wine or balsamic vinegar
>   1 tablespoon lemon juice
>   1 large clove of garlic, crushed
>   1 large pinch of mustard
>   Salt and pepper

Method:
1. The easiest way to combine these is to place all the ingredients into a clean, screw-top jar and shake to blend. The dressing can be made in advance, and even stored in the fridge for later.
2. On removing from the fridge, the dressing may look cloudy. Allow the oil to reach room temperature before shaking again and serving.

SWEET-AND-SOUR SALAD DRESSING

You can use this as a marinade as well as a salad dressing.

You will need:
>   60 g (2½ oz) sugar
>   40 ml (2½ tablespoons) rice wine vinegar
>   1 tablespoon diced onion
>   ¼ teaspoon garlic salt
>   Pepper and salt
>   120 ml (8 tablespoons) vegetable oil

Method:
1. Combine the sugar, vinegar, onion, salt and pepper and blend until smooth.
2. Pour in the oil in a slow, steady stream and mix until smooth, or use a screw-top jar to shake and mix.

ITALIAN DRESSING WITH SOUR CREAM

This is definitely not for weight watchers!

You will need:
> 110 ml (4 fluid oz) mayonnaise
> 110 ml (4 fluid oz) sour cream
> 2 tablespoons milk
> 1 tablespoon vinegar
> 1 clove crushed garlic
> ½ teaspoon dried marjoram
> ½ teaspoon dried basil
> ½ teaspoon honey
> ¼ teaspoon salt
> Black pepper

Method:
1. Combine all ingredients into a clean, screw-top jar. Shake until all the ingredients appear to have mixed.
2. Leave in the fridge for at least 2 hours before serving, but take out the jar about 10 minutes before you want to use the dressing and give it another shake.

Chutneys, Pickles & Preserves

CHEROKEE

This recipe dates from Victorian times and packs quite a punch.

You will need:

> 500 ml (1 pint) malt vinegar
> 4 tablespoons mushroom ketchup
> 2 tablespoons soy sauce
> 1 tablespoon cayenne pepper
> 2 cloves garlic, finely crushed or chopped

Method:

1. Put the ingredients into a large bottle, cork tightly and leave for 4 weeks.
2. Strain, or siphon, the clear liquid into clean bottles and seal.

SHALLOT SAUCE

You will need:

500 ml (1 pint) sherry
175 g (6 oz) shallots
¼ teaspoon cayenne pepper

Method:
1. Finely chop 100 g (4 oz) of the shallots and put them into a clean bottle with the sherry. Cover and leave for 10 days.
2. Strain off the liquid and replace in the bottle with the rest of the shallots, peeled but left whole. Add the cayenne, secure tightly and store for 6 weeks.
3. Strain again and store in smaller bottles for future use in salad dressings.

ESCAVEEKE SAUCE

There's certainly a hint of 'eek' here!

You will need:

575 ml (1 pint) white wine vinegar
The finely grated rind of 1 lemon
6 shallots, chopped
2 cloves of garlic, chopped
1 tablespoon coriander seeds
1 teaspoon ground ginger
½ teaspoon salt
½ level teaspoon cayenne pepper

Method:
1. Grind the coriander in a mortar and pestle. Add to the other dry ingredients and mix with the onions, garlic and lemon rind in a bowl.
2. Boil the vinegar and pour it over the onion mixture. When cold, bottle and seal.

PLUM AND ONION CHUTNEY

You will need:

    2 to 3 medium red onions, chopped
    700 g (1.5 lb) plums, stoned and cut into quarters
    80 g (3 oz) golden raisins
    40 g (2 oz) candied ginger, chopped
    225 g (8 oz) brown sugar
    150 ml (5 fluid oz) cider vinegar
    100 g (4 oz) hoisin sauce
    1 tablespoon mustard seed
    1 teaspoon salt

Method:
1. Put all the ingredients into a large pan, cover and bring to the boil.
2. Uncover and simmer for about 30 minutes, or until the sauce has thickened, stirring occasionally.
3. Pour hot chutney into sterilised jars and refrigerate for up to 2 weeks.

REFRIGERATOR GARLIC PICKLES

You will need:

    Whole, peeled garlic cloves
    1 tablespoon salt
    About 240 ml (8 fluid oz) red wine vinegar

Method:
1. Place the cloves of garlic in a jar with an air-tight lid. Add enough vinegar to cover, and add salt.
2. Place the lid on the jar and shake to dissolve the salt. Store in the refrigerator for 2 weeks before using.

THYME AND GARLIC PICKLE

This is for true garlic lovers. My eyes water just thinking about this, but here goes:

You will need:
- 2 whole heads garlic, divided into cloves
- ⅔ cup distilled white vinegar or white wine vinegar
- 3 tablespoons sugar
- ¼ teaspoon salt
- ½ teaspoon mixed pickling spice
- 3 sprigs fresh thyme, about 8 centimetres (3 inches) long

Method:
1. Peel the garlic and cut any large pieces in half lengthwise.
2. In a small saucepan, boil vinegar, sugar, salt and pickling spice. Add garlic cloves and return to the boil. Cook, stirring, for 1 minute.
3. Put thyme sprigs into a sterilised jar then pour in the garlic, liquid and spices, making sure the garlic is covered. Cover tightly. Leave to rest at room temperature for 24 hours to blend the flavours, then refrigerate for up to 2 months.

GARLIC OR SHALLOT PICKLE

This old recipe takes time and patience, but no refrigerator. It is not a last minute recipe.

You will need:
- 500 ml (1 pint) white wine vinegar
- 125 g (4 oz) shallots or garlic
- 30 g (1 oz) root ginger
- 30 g (1 oz) chillies
- 50 g (approx 2 oz) mustard seed
- 30 g (1 oz) turmeric
- 275 ml (½ pint) water
- 75 g (3 oz) salt

Method:
1. Firstly, boil the water and salt to create a brine, then pour over the root ginger. Leave for 5 days.
2. Remove the ginger, slice and dry it. Discard the brine.
3. Peel the shallots or garlic, sprinkle with salt and leave for 3 days.
4. Place the ginger, shallots or garlic, chillies, mustard and turmeric in a wide-necked bottle, pour over the vinegar and cover tightly. Store in a cool, dry place.

PICKLED ONIONS

Easy-peasy, and very tasty.

You will need:

> Pickling onions
> Vinegar
> Black peppercorns
> Allspice

Method:
1. Remove the skins from pickling onions, until the onions are clear and firm.
2. Place into clean, dry jars and cover immediately with vinegar. For each 500 ml, or pint, of vinegar used, add 1 teaspoon of black peppercorns and 1 teaspoon of allspice. Cover and store for 2 weeks, when they will be ready to eat.

PICCALILLI

You will need:

> 225 g (8 oz) cauliflower florets
> 125 g (4 oz) French beans
> 225 g (8 oz) pickling onions
> 225 g (8 oz) diced cucumber
> 125 g (4 oz) salt
> 1 teaspoon turmeric
> 3 teaspoons dry mustard
> ½ teaspoon ground ginger
> 75 g (3 oz) sugar

430 ml (¾ pint) malt vinegar
4 teaspoons cornflour

Method:
1. Put the vegetables, chopped and sliced, in a colander and add the salt. Leave to stand for as long as possible, then rinse and drain.
2. Mix the ginger, sugar, turmeric and mustard with a little of the vinegar. Add all but a few tablespoons of the remaining vinegar and put in a saucepan with the vegetables. Simmer gently for about 5 minutes. Don't let the vegetables go soggy.
3. Mix the remaining vinegar with the cornflour, add to the pan with the vegetables and bring to the boil, stirring carefully. After 3 minutes, spoon mix into the wide necked jars, cool and cover.

BASIL AND GARLIC VINEGAR

As mentioned earlier, garlic should not be stored in oil for long periods because of a slight risk of botulism, if left unrefrigerated. There is no problem with garlic in vinegar, however, so that's the way to go to speed up making dressings.

You will need:
1 clove garlic
450 ml (15 fluid oz) white wine vinegar
10 tablespoons chopped, fresh basil

Method:
1. Crush the garlic and add to the basil leaves. Mash them up together and put these in a heatproof bowl or pan.
2. Heat up half of the vinegar and pour it while boiling over the herbs. Mix together and leave to cool.
3. Add the rest of the vinegar and pour into a preserving jar. Seal and leave for 2 weeks, shaking occasionally.
4. Pour through a strainer or filter and re-bottle.

GARLIC VINEGAR

You will need:

 3—4 large cloves garlic
 450 ml (15 fluid oz) white wine vinegar

Method:
Follow the method on page 111, for Basil and Garlic Vinegar.

JALAPENO GARLIC VINEGAR

This is another old recipe, used in dressing for taco, tomato and onion salads, or when making salsa.

You will need:

 2 jalapeno peppers
 2 crushed cloves garlic
 500 ml (1 pint) wine or apple cider vinegar

Method:
1. Cut small slits in the peppers, and place in a clean pint jar with the garlic.
2. Heat the vinegar to just below boiling point. Fill a clean jar with the vinegar and cap tightly.
3. Allow this to stand for 3 to 4 weeks in a cool dark place.
4. Strain the vinegar, discarding the peppers and garlic, and pour into a sterilised jar. Seal tightly.

Breads & Snacks

GARLIC BREAD

This is so easy to do and a lot cheaper than the stuff you buy ready made. It also tastes better. You can substitute margarine, but sometimes it just has to be butter! You can make the garlic butter in advance if you are doing lots of loaves for a party.

You will need:
   1 French stick/baguette
   2 cloves garlic
   80 g (3 oz) butter, softened
   1 tablespoon chopped parsley (optional)

Method:
1. Slice the baguette in wide, diagonal slices, stopping just short of the bottom crust.
2. Peel and crush the garlic and beat into the butter. Add the parsley if using and mix together well.
3. Spread the garlic butter on each side of the slices of bread and spread any leftover butter on the top of the loaf.
4. Wrap the loaf in foil and bake for about 5–10 minutes in a moderately hot oven (200°C, 400°F, gas mark 6).

GARLIC FLAT BREAD

This sounds a lot more complicated than it really is. Like all bread-making, once you've made it a few times, it is easy! Once you have made the dough, you can put all sorts of toppings on and make a meal of it.

You will need:
- 240 g (8 oz) strong flour
- 25 g (1 oz) dried yeast
- 1 tablespoon soft brown sugar
- 150 ml (5 fluid oz) water
- 2 tablespoons olive oil

For the garlic butter:
- 100 g (4 oz) unsalted butter
- 4 cloves garlic, finely chopped
- Salt and black pepper

Method:
1. Mix the flour, yeast, sugar, water and olive oil together to form the dough. Knead the dough well for about 10 minutes and then set aside in a large bowl, covered with clingfilm. Leave to prove for approximately 30 minutes at room temperature, until the dough has almost doubled in size.
2. Push some of the air out of the dough by gently punching the dough in the bowl a few times and then turn onto a lightly floured board. Roll out the dough to form a thin base.
3. Dust your fingers with flour and lightly press them into the dough to make depressions to hold some of the garlic butter while it cooks.
4. Leave this to prove again for about 20 minutes.
5. To prepare the garlic butter, melt the butter in a pan and add the chopped garlic, salt and pepper.
6. Preheat the oven to 220°C (425°F, gas mark 7). Brush some of the garlic butter over the bread and bake for about 10 minutes or until golden brown.
7. Remove from the oven and while still hot, pour over the rest of the garlic butter. Serve immediately.

FRENCH BREAD CANAPÉS

There are several variations to these delicious, crispy accompaniments to an aperitif. The addition of vinegar adds a little tang, and it's a great way to use up stale pieces of bread.

You will need:
>1 large baguette, or similar French stick
>150 ml (5 fluid oz) olive oil
>4 cloves crushed garlic
>1 tbsp balsamic vinegar
>2 tbsp chopped parsley or other herbs, e.g. basil
>225 g (8 oz) cheese of your choice
>4 or 5 tomatoes

Method:
1. Slice the loaf fairly thickly. Mix the garlic with the olive oil and brush the bread on both sides with this mixture.
2. Slice the tomatoes thinly and brush with a little oil.
3. Grill the bread on both sides and place a slice of tomato on each piece of toast. Drizzle with balsamic vinegar, sprinkle with chopped herbs, then cheese, and return to the grill until the cheese melts.
4. Serve immediately with a glass of wine.

HUMMOUS

This Middle Eastern favourite is in great demand in our house. It is a good healthy starter, being made with chickpeas. You need to plan ahead to cook the chickpeas first. There is a quicker version below.

You will need:
>125 g (4 oz) dried chickpeas
>2 tablespoons tahini
>2 cloves garlic, crushed
>½ lemon, juiced
>2 tablespoons olive oil
>Salt and pepper
>Fresh mint to garnish

Method:

1. Soak the chickpeas overnight. Drain them and put in a pan, covered in cold water.

2. Bring to the boil and simmer for 2 hours, until soft.

3. Drain the chickpeas, but keep the water.

4. Blend the chickpeas with the tahini, garlic, and 100 ml (4 fluid oz) of the liquid from the chickpeas, the lemon juice and ½ teaspoon salt. Add a good couple of pinches of black pepper.

5. Serve with bread or oat biscuits.

HUMMOUS WITH CORIANDER AND PITTA BREAD

This uses tinned chickpeas, so is a good standby version. If the extra garlic for the pitta bread is too much, you can leave it out.

You will need: Serves 4

    1 clove garlic, roughly chopped

    1 red chilli, seeded and roughly chopped

    ½ bunch fresh coriander, roughly chopped

    1 can chickpeas, drained

    juice of ½ lime

    2 tablespoons olive oil

    salt and freshly ground black pepper

For the garlic pitta:

    3 tablespoons olive oil

    2 cloves garlic, crushed (optional)

    1 tablespoon fresh parsley, chopped

    4 white pitta breads

Method:

1. Blend the garlic, chilli and coriander in a food processor with the chickpeas.

2. Add the lime juice and the oil to make a coarse paste. Season well and put into a serving bowl.

3. Mix together the olive oil, garlic, parsley and seasoning. Put the pitta breads under a hot grill for about 1 minute until browned. Turn over the bread and cut the softer, upper surface 4–5 times. Don't cut all the way through.

4. Brush with the herb and oil mixture and return to the grill for another minute.
5. Cool the bread, break or chop up and serve with the hummous.

TAPENADE

This paste of crushed olives and garlic is another staple for nibbles in France, served with toasted baguette or breadsticks. I like it on mini oat biscuits best, but if you use bread, drizzle a little olive oil on and grill slices of bread for a minute or two each side.

You will need:
    50 g (2 oz) black olives, pitted
    Salt and black pepper
    2 tablespoons olive oil
    1 garlic clove, crushed
    fresh chives, to garnish

Method:
1. Place the olives, seasoning and two tablespoons of the olive oil into a mini food processor and blend together until smooth.
2. Spread the tapenade on toast or biscuits and garnish with chives.

CHICKEN LIVER PÂTÉ

This has got to be the best value for money starter or snack dish, as well as being highly nutritious. Nobody will believe it only cost just over £1 to make! Frozen chicken livers are even cheaper, but you must thaw them well first.

You will need: Serves 4—6
- 1 packet fresh chicken livers
- 1 small onion, chopped
- 1 clove garlic, crushed
- 25 g (1 oz) butter
- Pepper and salt
- 2 tablespoons cream or crème fraiche
- 1 teaspoon tomato purée (optional)

Method:
1. Drain the chicken livers and pat dry with kitchen paper.
2. Heat the butter in a large frying pan and put in the onions, garlic and chicken livers. Keep the heat high and stir the livers frequently for about 5 minutes. Cover the pan, remove from the heat and let it rest and cool.
3. Blend the cooled livers with the cream, tomato purée and seasoning in a food processor until almost smooth. A few lumps are good to give texture.
4. Turn into ramekin dishes and press down with a fork. When completely cool, refrigerate for at least an hour before serving.

Main Course Dishes

MEAT DISHES

VEGETARIAN DISHES

FISH DISHES

MEAT DISHES

CHINESE GARLIC CHICKEN

You will need: Serves 4

    4 boneless, skinless chicken breasts

    1 egg white

    1 tablespoon cornflour

    1 tablespoon dry sherry

    4 spring onions, sliced very thinly, diagonally

    1 teaspoon chopped root ginger

    4 medium cloves garlic, finely chopped

    2 tablespoons vegetable oil

For the sauce:

    1 teaspoon chilli paste

    2 teaspoons sugar

    1 teaspoon cornflour

    2 teaspoons rice vinegar

    1 tablespoon water

    2 tablespoons dry sherry

    2 tablespoons soy sauce

Method:

1. Thinly slice the chicken breasts into fine slivers.

2. Beat the egg white lightly and then mix in the cornflour and sherry. Stir well until the cornflour dissolves.

3. Add the chicken to the egg and cornflour mix to coat all the pieces. Leave this to stand at room temperature for about 30 minutes.

4. Mix all the sauce ingredients together.

5. Heat your wok or frying pan, add the oil and stir-fry the chicken until thoroughly cooked. Remove the chicken with a slotted spoon.

6. Add the onions, ginger and garlic to the pan and stir-fry for about 30 seconds, until you can smell the spices but they are not brown. Return the chicken to the pan and add the sauce. Stirring constantly, cook until the food is well combined, hot and bubbly and the sauce thickens slightly. Serve immediately.

LIVER AND ONIONS

Having had a few bad experiences with school dinner liver, or leather, in the old days, I've recently become a born-again liver eater. I still can't convince my son, who had an even worse school dinner experience (don't ask), but at least he likes the chicken liver pâté in the snacks section. This is very quick and easy. You could add bacon, but I think this is great without.

You will need: **Serves 3—4**

    350 g (12 oz) lamb's liver
    4 medium sized onions, sliced
    2 cloves garlic
    225 ml (8 fluid oz) red wine
    100 ml (4 fluid oz) water
    2 tablespoons balsamic vinegar
    2 tablespoons olive oil
    Salt and pepper

Method:

1. Heat half the oil in a frying pan and put in the onions. Cook until they start to turn brown. Add the garlic and stir well, still keeping the heat up.

2. Add the wine, water and vinegar and then lower the heat. Simmer gently for about 40 minutes. Season with pepper and salt.

3. Prepare the liver by slicing very thinly into small strips. Heat the rest of the oil in another pan and put in the liver slices. They will only take a couple of minutes, so don't leave them or they may get dry and overcooked.
4. Put the liver onto a heated plate and pour over the onions and sauce. Delicious!

LAMB AND CASHEW BURGERS

These have become a regular favourite for barbecues at our house. They have changed in recipe from, originally, neck of lamb, to ready-bought, minced lamb, but either will do. I've just gone for ease and speed. You need some fat to stop the lamb drying out.

You will need: Serves 4—6
    350 g (12 oz) lean minced lamb
    1 medium onion, chopped roughly
    1 clove garlic, chopped
    100 g (4 oz) unsalted cashew nuts
    ½ bunch fresh coriander
    Juice of ½ lime
    Pepper
    ½ green chilli (optional)
    1 teaspoon ground coriander
    1 teaspoon ground cumin

Method:
1. Put the onion, garlic, chilli, nuts and the fresh coriander into a food processor and chop together.
2. Add the meat, lime juice and spices. Mix until just combined, but so that you can still see some nuts and coriander showing through.
3. Take large tablespoons of the mix and press them into flattened balls with your hands. The size and number you make depend on you. Bigger ones are less likely to fall apart.
4. Put the burgers onto a plate and refrigerate until you are ready to cook. Take the burgers out when you light the barbecue to return to room temperature before cooking.

TURKEY SLICES WITH
ONIONS AND MUSTARD SAUCE

This is another Briggs standard dish. I vary the meat and sometimes use pork chops instead, but turkey is so much better for you. If using pork chops, I put the meat and onions in the oven for about 35 minutes instead, then finish off the sauce on the top.

You will need: Serves 3—4

    350 g (12 oz) turkey escallops
    2 medium onions
    1 tablespoon olive oil
    1 teaspoon English mustard
    2 tablespoons crème fraiche
    Black pepper

Method:
1. Slice the onions thinly and heat the oil in a large pan. Cook the onions until they start to go black round the edges.
2. Add the turkey slices, placing them on top of the layer of onions. Cook, turning occasionally until the turkey is cooked through. Remove the meat to a heated plate.
3. The onions will probably be stuck to the pan, but that doesn't matter. Add the crème fraiche and the mustard and stir in with a wooden spoon. The onions will mix in and the caramel bits in the pan will give the sauce a lovely rich colour with the mustard. Pour over the turkey and serve.

INDIAN LAMB WITH ONIONS AND GARLIC

Another firm family favourite. Preparation takes time, but the result is worth it and the garlic is not dominant in this wonderful mixture of spices.

You will need: Serves 4

3 large onions
5 cloves garlic
1 tablespoon grated fresh ginger
225 ml (8 fluid oz) water
6 tablespoons vegetable oil
6 cardamom pods
6 whole cloves
Small piece of stick cinnamon
700 g (1.5 lb) cubed shoulder of lamb
2 teaspoons ground coriander
2 teaspoons ground cumin
Pinch of cayenne pepper
½ teaspoon salt
4–5 tablespoons plain yoghurt

Method:
1. Cut two of the onions into fine half-rings and chop the third one finely. Keep separate.
2. Put the garlic, ginger and a spoonful of water into a food processor and blend to a paste.
3. Heat the oil in a large pan and fry the sliced onions until brown. Remove from the pan and drain on kitchen paper. Put the whole spices into the oil and then enough meat to cover the base of the pan. Brown this meat, remove to a plate and add the rest of the meat to the pan to brown before removing.
4. Add the chopped onion, stirring until it turns brown. Add the ground spices and the garlic-ginger paste. Add the yoghurt, one spoon at a time, and stir with a wooden spoon.
5. Return all the meat and juices to the pan, with the water and salt. Cover and simmer for about 40 minutes. You can put it in the oven on a medium heat (190°C, 375°F, gas mark 5) if you prefer.
6. Just before serving, add the fried onions and check the seasoning. Serve with plain rice and green beans in garlic (see below).

ROAST CHICKEN WITH 40 CLOVES OF GARLIC

Don't be alarmed at the number of garlic cloves. The garlic keeps the chicken really moist, and garlic has quite a different taste in this form. I always put whole cloves of garlic under the skin of the turkey at Christmas to stop it drying out.

You will need:

1.8 kg (4 lb) whole chicken
½ teaspoon salt
¼ teaspoon black pepper
25 g (1 oz) butter
1 sprig rosemary
1 sprig thyme
1 sprig sage
1 bay leaf
40 garlic cloves, peeled (from 3 to 4 heads of garlic)

Method:
1. Preheat oven to 190°C (375°F, gas mark 5).
2. Rinse chicken and pat it dry. Sprinkle the inside and out with salt and pepper and place about six of the cloves inside the chicken with the sprigs of herbs. Cover the bird with butter and place in a roasting tin, covered, for 30 minutes.
3. Add the rest of the garlic to the pan, baste the bird and roast for another 40 minutes or until the juices run clear. Remove the foil or lid for the last few minutes to brown the chicken.
4. Allow the chicken to rest for 15 minutes in the pan, then remove the bird to a warm plate to carve.
5. Reheat the juices and herbs. Remove the sprigs of herbs and skim off the fat, but leave the garlic in the sauce. Serve with toast or baguette.

ROGAN JOSH

This is a hotter, red curry. If the quantities of chilli and paprika are too much, adjust to taste.

You will need: Serves 4-6

6 garlic cloves, roughly chopped
1 large onion, roughly chopped
1 teaspoon dried ginger
1 teaspoon ground cinnamon
2 teaspoons ground cumin
2 teaspoons ground coriander
1 tablespoon paprika
1 teaspoon chilli powder
1 teaspoon salt
1 tablespoon tomato purée
4 tablespoons vegetable oil
1 kg (2 lb) neck of lamb, cut into bite-size cubes
8–10 cardamom pods, lightly crushed with the back of
   a spoon
275 ml (10 fluid oz) water

Method:
1. Blend the onion, garlic and a spoonful of the water in a food processor.
2. Heat the oil in a large pan and fry the lamb in batches to brown, removing each batch with a slotted spoon. Brown all the meat and keep on a plate.
3. Add the cardamom pods, followed by the onions and garlic. Be careful in case of spitting from the pan. Stir in the dried spices, salt and tomato purée.
4. Return the lamb to the pan with any juices that have accumulated on the plate. Stir well.
5. Pour in the water, lower the heat and simmer for about an hour, until the lamb is tender. You need to stir occasionally during the cooking time and check to see that the pot hasn't lost all of the liquid.

CAULIFLOWER WITH ONION, GARLIC AND BACON

I had almost forgotten about this recipe, which used to be one of our favourite family ways of serving cauliflower, especially with roast chicken. The crunchy texture goes well with the bacon and garlic. Of course, for vegetarians, leave out the bacon (and the chicken!).

You will need:
>   1 medium onion, chopped
>   1 clove garlic, crushed
>   2 tablespoons olive oil
>   2 rashers streaky bacon, chopped
>   2 tablespoons breadcrumbs
>   2 tablespoons chopped parsley
>   1 medium cauliflower

Method:
1. Separate the cauliflower into florets and cook in boiling water for 4 minutes. Drain immediately.
2. Meanwhile, in a pan, heat the oil and fry the bacon with the onion and garlic until brown. Mix in the breadcrumbs and the parsley.
3. Put the cauliflower into an ovenproof dish and spoon over the contents of the pan.
4. Cook for 15–20 minutes at 190°C (375°F, gas mark 5), or put into the oven with the roast for the last 15 minutes.

CHILLI CON CARNE

This recipe uses minced beef, but I often substitute lamb or turkey mince for recipes such as this. I'm not supposed to eat a lot of red meat, so turkey, being a superfood and very lean, is ideal (and very economical). You can cook this in an oven, or on the hob.

You will need: Serves 4

350 g (12 oz) onions, sliced
2 tablespoons oil
1 tablespoon wine vinegar
450 g (1 lb) minced beef, or turkey
1 teaspoon caraway seeds (optional)
1 teaspoon marjoram
Pinch of chilli powder (or to taste)
1 tin tomatoes
1 tin red kidney beans
1 green pepper
285 ml (10 fluid oz) water
Black pepper

Method:
1. If cooking in an oven, preheat to 180°C (350°F, gas mark 4). Heat the oil and vinegar into a large pan or ovenproof casserole. Add the onions and cook them slowly in the liquid until they are almost tender.
2. Add the mince and stir to break up. Brown the meat evenly and add the caraway, marjoram and chilli powder.
3. Slice the pepper and add to the mince with the tinned tomatoes, water and seasoning.
4. Drain the kidney beans and wash away the liquid by placing them in a sieve or colander. Add to the pan.
5. Cook for 45 minutes in the oven, or simmer gently, covered, on the hob. Remove the lid if there is too much liquid, to reduce the sauce.

BOEUF BOURGIGNON

This classic French casserole can be made ahead and frozen or kept chilled in the fridge and reheated, making it ideal for large gatherings by increasing the quantities. It is best cooked slowly, so is ideal for the bottom of an Aga.

You will need: Serves 4–6
    900 g (2 lb) braising or stewing steak,
        cut into 5 cm (2 inch) chunks
    2 cloves garlic, chopped
    1 medium onion, chopped
    350 g (12 oz) shallots or baby onions
    Sprig of fresh thyme
    2 bay leaves
    225 g (8 oz) streaky bacon, chopped
    3 tablespoons olive oil
    1 heaped tablespoon plain flour
    425 ml (15 fluid oz) red wine
    4 oz (110 g) mushrooms, cut into chunks
    Salt and black pepper

Method:
1. Preheat the oven to 140°C (275°F, gas mark 1).
2. In a large, ovenproof casserole heat up half the oil and fry the beef in batches to seal it. Remove with a slotted spoon to a plate.
3. Add the chopped onion and garlic to brown and then return the meat and juices to the casserole.
4. Stir in the flour and then pour a little of the wine in, stirring continuously.
5. Pour in the rest of the wine, herbs and seasoning.
6. Cover and cook for 2 hours. Just before time's up, heat up the rest of the oil in a pan and fry the shallots or small onions (whole) and the bacon. Check that there is enough liquid left.
7. Add to the casserole and return to the oven for another hour. Serve with roast or new potatoes and broccoli.

CHICKEN BREASTS IN HERB SAUCE

This is a very lean, healthy way to cook chicken, although you need a few pans to cook the separate parts.

You will need: **Serves 4**
    1 medium onion, sliced
    1 leek, halved lengthways and sliced
    1 carrot, sliced
    4 boneless chicken breasts
    1 bay leaf
    2 tablespoons chopped parsley
    1 stick celery, chopped
    1 teaspoon salt
    10 black peppercorns
    225 g (8 oz) noodles
    25 g (1 oz) butter

For the herb sauce:
    100 g (4 oz) sorrel or spinach (washed)
    1 bunch watercress
    25 g (1 oz) butter
    2 tablespoons flour
    150 ml (5 fluid oz) single cream
    1 tablespoon chopped tarragon
    1 tablespoon chopped parsley
    Salt and pepper

Method:
1. Place the onions, leek, carrot and celery with the bay leaf, parsley and peppercorns in a large saucepan. Just cover with cold water and bring to the boil.
2. Put in the chicken breasts and lower the heat. Cover and simmer for 30 minutes.
3. Lift out the chicken and keep warm. Strain the stock and keep 285 ml (10 fluid oz) for the sauce.
4. Cook the noodles, following the advice on the packet.
5. To make the sauce, cook the sorrel or spinach by steaming or dropping in boiling water briefly. Drain and press, then chop.
6. Cook the watercress tops in the same way, and chop roughly.

7. Melt the butter in a pan and add the flour, stirring to a paste. Add the measured, strained stock and stir until thickened. Add the cream and simmer for a couple of minutes.

8. Cool slightly and blend the sauce with the sorrel/spinach, parsley, tarragon and watercress to make a fine, lump-free sauce. Reheat with seasoning.

9. Serve the chicken on a bed of noodles, covered in herb sauce.

ORIENTAL BEEF WITH
ONIONS AND GREEN PEPPERS

Two types of onions combine to add a distinctive flavour to this dish.

You will need: Serves 3—4

   450 g (1lb) beef steak
   2 medium onions, chopped
   1 clove garlic, crushed
   1 teaspoon freshly grated ginger
   3 tablespoons water
   2 large spring onions, sliced diagonally
   Oil for stir-frying

For the marinade:

   2 tablespoons light soy sauce
   1 tablespoon dry sherry
   A few drops of sesame oil
   Black pepper, to taste
   2 teaspoons cornflour

For the sauce:

   3 tablespoons dark soy sauce
   1 tablespoon sugar
   1 tablespoon dry sherry

Method:

1. Cut the beef into strips across the grain. Mix the marinade ingredients in a bowl and marinate the beef for about 15 minutes.

2. Combine the sauce ingredients in a small bowl and leave aside.

3. Heat 2 tablespoons of oil in a wok or frying pan and add ginger and garlic. Stir-fry briefly and add the chopped onions. Stir-fry until the onions are tender, but not overcooked. Remove the vegetables from the wok and leave aside.

4. Add 2 more tablespoons of oil to the wok. Add the beef, stir-frying until it changes colour. Add water at this point to make a gravy.

5. Return the vegetables to the wok and mix well. Add the sauce and stir in the spring onions. Stir-fry just to blend all the flavours. Serve hot with rice.

VEGETARIAN DISHES

GARLIC OMELETTE

This omelette will serve two people. The parsley will help to cover the garlic breath!

You will need:

4—5 eggs
1 large clove garlic
50 g (2 oz) butter
2 slices dry bread
Salt and pepper
1 tablespoon chopped parsley

Method:

1. Take the crusts off the bread and cut it into croutons (small cubes).
2. Crush the garlic and put most of the butter into a pan. Fry the croutons in the pan with the garlic until brown. Remove to a plate.
3. Beat the eggs together and season with salt and pepper. Put the rest of the butter into the pan and reheat.
4. Pour the eggs into the hot pan and as soon as they start to set, add the garlic croutons. Cook quickly, then turn out onto a plate, folding the omelette. Add the parsley and eat while piping hot.

POTATO SALAD

This is a good salad for barbecues. If you like beetroot, you can add a small cooked beet to the potatoes.

You will need:
  4 medium new potatoes, unpeeled
  1 small cooked beetroot (optional)
  2 tablespoons red wine vinegar
  2 tablespoons olive oil
  1 tablespoon lemon juice
  1 garlic clove, crushed
  Finely chopped fresh parsley
  3 spring onions, chopped
  1 tablespoon chopped fresh dill
  2 tablespoons finely chopped fresh mint
  Pepper to taste
  Paprika

Method:
1. Cook the potatoes for about 20 minutes, until tender.
2. Drain but do not peel, and dice as soon as cool enough to handle. Place in a serving bowl.
3. Put the vinegar, oil, lemon juice and garlic in a screw-top jar and shake until combined. Mix the dressing lightly with the potatoes and allow to cool. Add beetroot, if liked.
4. When completely cool, toss in the parsley, onions, dill, mint and pepper. Serve at room temperature, sprinkled with a little paprika. (You can vary the herbs as you like.)

PIPERADE

This Mediterranean dish can be serve at any time of day, for a spicy breakfast, lunch or supper dish.

You will need: **Serves 2**

    1 onion, sliced
    1 red pepper, seeded and sliced
    1 green pepper, seeded and sliced
    2 cloves garlic, crushed
    4 tomatoes, sliced, or ½ tin tomatoes, drained
    4 eggs
    Salt and pepper
    1 tablespoon milk
    1 tablespoon cooking oil

Method:
1. Heat the oil and fry the onion and peppers until soft but not brown.
2. Add the garlic, tomatoes and seasoning. Simmer for about 5 minutes.
3. Beat the eggs with the milk and pour into the pan, cooking and stirring until the eggs start to set.
4. Serve immediately, with toast or crusty bread.

CHEESE AND ONION OAT FLAN

I love this combination of cheese and onion, although there's a lot of fat, what with the cheese, milk and margarine. Using skimmed milk will keep down the fat, and you could use a low fat cheese, as long as it doesn't taste like soap.

You will need:

120 g (4 oz) wholemeal flour
120 g (4 oz) oatmeal
120 g (4 oz) margarine
Water for mixing
Pinch of salt
2 eggs
3 chopped onions
150 ml (¼ pint) skimmed milk
225 g (8 oz) grated cheese of your choice
Pepper

Method:
1. Put the flour, salt and oatmeal into a large bowl and rub in the margarine. Add enough water to mix to a firm dough.
2. Turn onto a floured surface, knead and roll out to line a flan dish. Put in the fridge while you make the filling.
3. Heat some oil in a pan to fry the chopped onions. Fry until they start to turn brown.
4. Beat the eggs and add the milk, then the onions and most of the cheese.
5. Put into the pastry crust, add the rest of the cheese and a good pinch or grinding of pepper.
6. Bake at 190°C (375°F, gas mark 5) for about 35 minutes.

VEGETABLE KEBABS

These are another favourite for barbecues. I get to eat lots of vegetables and any vegetarians don't feel left out. The vegetables vary, depending on what's growing or what we have in, but you can choose from the suggestions below. They go well with the lamb and cashew burgers, above. If it rains, just put the whole lot of vegetables into a baking tray and cook in the oven for about 20 minutes.

You will need: **For 4 large (metal) kebabs**

  12 cherry tomatoes
  3 medium onions or 8 shallots
  2 green peppers (or other colours)
  8 chestnut mushrooms
  1 small aubergine
  2 small courgettes
  1 tablespoon olive oil
  2 tablespoons balsamic vinegar

Method:
1. Wash the vegetables. Prepare the aubergine by slicing thickly, then halving each slice. If you have time, leave the slices in a colander with salt sprinkled over to drain for half an hour.
2. Cut the courgettes into thick slices. Halve and quarter the peppers. Cut each section in half if they are big.
3. Thread the vegetables in colourful strings, with the tomatoes and mushrooms left whole.
4. Leave to rest on a large plate. Pour over the balsamic vinegar and brush with oil before cooking.

SPINACH WITH POTATOES AND ONIONS

This is an easy dish to make and can be very filling, ideal for a cold winter's night. Serve with other Indian dishes or roast lamb.

You will need: **Serves 4**

    350 g (12 oz) potatoes, peeled and cubed
    350 g (12 oz) fresh spinach leaves, washed and chopped
    110 g (4 oz) onions, chopped
    2 cloves garlic, crushed
    2 tablespoons oil
    1 teaspoon ground cumin seeds
    1 teaspoon ground coriander seeds
    1 teaspoon whole black mustard seeds
    Pinch cayenne pepper
    Salt
    150 ml (5 fluid oz) water

Method:

1. Heat the oil in a thick-bottomed pan. Add the black mustard seeds and cook until they start to pop. Add the onions and garlic and fry for 2–3 minutes.

2. Add the potatoes, cayenne and other spices. Fry and stir to combine. Add the spinach, salt and 2 tablespoons of water. Bring to the boil and then add the rest of the water. Cover and lower the heat.

3. Cook until the potatoes are tender – about 20 minutes. Check that the liquid has not all been absorbed and adjust if necessary.

GREEN BEANS IN GARLIC

If you ever get fed up with boiled or steamed French beans, try this version.

You will need: Serves 4

    450 g (1 lb) French beans
    3 tablespoons vegetable oil
    1 tablespoon whole black mustard seeds
    2 cloves garlic, crushed
    ½ green chilli, finely chopped (optional)
    1 teaspoon salt
    Black pepper

Method:
1. Top and tail the beans, wash them and cut them in half. Put them into boiling water for about 3 minutes to parboil. Drain and cool.
2. Heat the oil in a frying pan and put in the mustard seeds. As soon as they start to pop, add the garlic and chilli. Stir for a few moments and then add the green beans and salt.
3. Cook for about 5–6 minutes, over a low heat, stirring and turning the beans. Season with pepper and serve.

POTATO AND ONION RISSOLES

You will need:

    450 g (1 lb) potatoes, peeled
    2 onions, chopped
    1 egg
    75 g (3 oz) grated Cheddar cheese
    100 g (4 oz) oatmeal
    Salt and pepper

Method:
1. Boil and mash the potatoes and mix with the onion, cheese, seasoning and half of a beaten egg. Allow to cool.
2. When cool, shape into patties, dip in the remaining egg, then in oatmeal to coat.
3. Cook the patties in vegetable or olive oil for 2–3 minutes on each side, until brown.

ROASTED GARLIC

You will need:
> Whole heads of garlic
> 1 tablespoon olive oil per head

Method:
1. Preheat the oven to 190°C (375°F, gas mark 5).
2. Take off the loose, papery layers but leave the bulbs whole.
3. Place on foil and pour over the olive oil. Wrap into a parcel and cook for about 35 minutes. Cool slightly.
4. Squeeze the garlic out of the bulbs and use to fill jacket potatoes or spread on toast.

GARLIC MASHED POTATOES

You will need:
> 4 large potatoes peeled and chopped into large pieces
> 25 g (1 oz) butter
> 2 tablespoons cream
> 2 cloves garlic
> Salt and pepper

Method:
1. Bring the potatoes to the boil and simmer until tender.
2. Roughly chop the garlic and simmer it in the cream and butter for about three minutes. Remove the pieces of garlic with a slotted spoon.
3. Mash the cooked potatoes or pass through a ricer. Add the cream and mix until smooth. Add salt and pepper to taste.

LEEK AND EGG BAKE

This is quite substantial as a lunch or supper dish. If you want to, you can serve it with bacon or grilled sausages, for any hearty carnivore who can't do without!

You will need: Serves 4

 4 eggs
 2 leeks
 ½ pint milk
 1 level tablespoon plain flour
 50 g (2 oz) grated cheese
 Salt and a pinch of cayenne pepper
 25 g (1 oz) butter or margarine

Method:
1. Put the eggs on to boil for 10 minutes.
2. Meanwhile, prepare the leeks by washing carefully, slicing in half and then cutting into 2 cm (1 inch) lengths. Parboil for 5 minutes and drain immediately.
3. Make a sauce as follows: heat the butter or margarine in a saucepan until melted and then stir in the flour. This will make a thick paste. Gradually add the milk, stirring all the time. You may need to remove the pan from the heat to stop it burning. Stir until the sauce thickens evenly. If it gets lumpy, keep stirring. Add most of the grated cheese and the cayenne pepper. Set aside until you are ready for the next step.
4. Peel the boiled eggs and cut them in half. Put the leeks into an ovenproof dish and place the eggs on top. Pour over the cheese sauce and top with the rest of the cheese.
5. Brown under a hot grill and serve.

SPICY SPINACH WITH ONIONS

I love using spices in cooking. This dish is equally good with other spicy dishes or with roast chicken, and is an ideal way of using up a glut of perpetual spinach.

You will need: **Serves 4**

    1 kg (2 lb) spinach, washed and cut into strips
    2 medium onions, finely chopped
    1 teaspoon fresh ginger, grated or finely chopped
    ½ hot green chilli (optional)
    4 tablespoons oil
    ½ teaspoon salt
    Pinch of sugar
    125 ml (3 fluid oz) water

Method:
1. Heat the oil in a large pan and stir in the onions. Add the spinach, ginger, salt, sugar and chilli. Stir and cook for about 5 minutes.
2. Add the water to the pan and cover tightly. Continue to cook over a very low heat for another 5 minutes.
3. Remove the lid and boil away any excess liquid before serving.

GREEK MUSHROOMS

These can be served as a starter or side dish. This dish is ideal to make in advance as it is served cold.

You will need: Serves 4

    350 g (12 oz) firm button mushrooms
    5 tablespoons white wine
    5 tablespoons water
    5 tablespoons olive oil
    Bay leaf
    1 tablespoon chopped onion or shallot
    1 clove garlic, sliced
    Juice of half a lemon
    1 teaspoon thyme
    1 teaspoon fennel seeds
    1 tablespoon chopped coriander
    Salt and pepper

Method:
1. Wipe the mushrooms, but do not peel them. If the mushrooms are small leave them whole, if slightly larger, cut in halves or quarters.
2. Put the remaining ingredients except the coriander into a saucepan. Simmer for 5 minutes.
3. Add the mushrooms and simmer for 5 minutes. Let them cool in the liquid.
4. To serve, place in a bowl and add the chopped coriander.

AUBERGINES IN A SPICY SAUCE

This is a quick way to make an interesting sauce to accompany cold meat or barbecued sausages. Aubergines soak up a lot of oil, so you could treat them with salt in a colander first, as described for vegetable kebabs. If not, be prepared to use more oil and then skim some off before serving.

You will need: **Serves 4**

> 2 aubergines
> 110 ml (4 fluid oz) oil
> 4 spring onions
> 2 cloves garlic
> 1 teaspoon fresh ginger, grated
> 225 ml (8 fluid oz) tomato ketchup
> 1 tablespoon hot chilli sauce or barbecue sauce
> ½ teaspoon salt
> 1 tablespoon chopped fresh coriander
> 150 ml (5 fluid oz) water

Method:
1. Slice the aubergines and cut each slice into halves or quarters. Heat half the oil and fry the aubergines on both sides in batches, adding more oil for the second batch.
2. Remove with a slotted spoon and drain.
3. Chop the spring onions and add to the pan with the garlic and fresh ginger. Stir and fry for 2 minutes.
4. Stir in the ketchup and the hot chilli sauce, water and salt.
5. Return the aubergines to the pan and simmer for about 10 minutes until the aubergines are tender and the sauce has thickened.
6. Serve, garnished with the coriander.

SPINACH TART

You can make this quickly and easily, especially if you use ready-made pastry.

You will need:

    110 g (4 oz) shortcrust pastry

    1 medium onion or 2 shallots

    2 eggs

    225 g (8 oz) cooked spinach, chopped finely and
       well drained

    Salt and freshly ground pepper

    Large pinch grated nutmeg

    175 g (6 oz) Gruyere cheese, sliced thinly

    110 ml (4 fluid oz) single cream

Method:

1. Preheat the oven to 180°C (350°F, gas mark 4) and grease a flan dish or tin.

2. Roll out the pastry to line the flan dish.

3. Melt the butter in a pan and gently cook the onion.

4. Beat the eggs with the cream and stir in the onion and spinach. Season with the salt, pepper and nutmeg.

5. Put half of the cheese on top of the pastry and then pour in the spinach mixture. Finish with the rest of the cheese.

6. Bake for about 30 minutes, until golden. Serve hot or cold.

PASTA WITH HERBS AND GARLIC

If you haven't got fresh marjoram, use half the quantity of dried marjoram. This is a very quick dish to make.

You will need: **Serves 4**

    350 g (12 oz) pasta shapes of your choice
    3 tablespoons olive oil
    5 cloves garlic, crushed
    4 tablespoons chopped fresh marjoram
    3 tablespoons chopped parsley
    1 tablespoon chopped chives
    2 tablespoons lemon juice
    Salt and black pepper
    25 g (1 oz) butter
    Grated Parmesan cheese

Method:
1. Cook the pasta in boiling salted water according to directions on the packet. Drain, stir in the butter and keep hot.
2. Heat the oil in a pan and fry the garlic for a minute. Add the herbs and lemon juice.
3. Combine with the pasta in a large bowl and serve immediately with Parmesan cheese.

LEEK FRITTERS WITH GARLIC

You will need: **Serves 4-6**

  4 large leeks, cleaned, white part only
  3 cloves crushed garlic
  1 tablespoon chopped parsley
  1 tablespoon oil
  1 tablespoon flour
  Salt and pepper
  3 eggs, beaten
  Oil for frying

Method:

1. Slit the leeks in half lengthways and thinly slice them.
2. Heat a large frying pan and add the tablespoon of oil, garlic and leeks. Fry quickly for 3 minutes. Remove to a bowl to cool.
3. Add the remaining ingredients to the bowl and mix together well.
4. Heat a large non-stick frying pan and add the oil for frying. Drop tablespoons of the fritter mixture into the hot pan. Flatten each one slightly and fry over medium heat until golden brown on both sides.
5. Remove when cooked and cook all of the fritters. Add more oil if necessary. Drain on paper towels and serve hot.

LATKES

I made these at school once to celebrate the Jewish festival of Hanukah with my class. They were very popular! If fried in deep oil they will be puffy and crispy, but you can cook them in shallow oil, or even in the oven (see below).

You will need: **Serves 4—6**

    6 medium potatoes
    1 medium onion
    2 eggs, beaten
    1 teaspoon salt
    50 g (2 oz) flour
    Oil for frying

Method:
1. Peel the potatoes and onion and grate them. This is much easier in a food processor.
2. Squeeze out the liquid. Add the eggs, flour and salt and stir to make a batter.
3. Heat the oil in a large frying pan, preferably non-stick. Drop in spoonfuls of the batter and fry over a moderate heat until the latkes are golden brown. Turn and fry the other side. Remove and drain on kitchen paper. Repeat with the rest of the batch.

These pancakes may also be baked in a shallow pan for 45 minutes at 180°C (350°F, gas mark 4) until nicely browned. Cut into squares and serve hot.

FISH DISHES

MACKEREL LYONNAISE

This makes a great lunch dish. It is very easy to prepare and even French friends rave about it. A regular treat from the market fish stall!

You will need: **Serves 4**

> 4 large fresh mackerel, cleaned and de-headed
> 2 medium onions, sliced into rings
> 4–6 large fresh tomatoes, sliced
> 4 tablespoons red wine vinegar
> 2 tablespoons olive oil

Method:
1. In a large pan, heat the oil and fry the onions until brown. Remove to a plate.
2. Put in the fish, cover and cook for about 5 minutes each side. The actual time will depend on the size of the fish.
3. Just before they are cooked through, return the onions to the pan and add the sliced tomatoes. Pour over the vinegar and let it all simmer for a few minutes, until the juices have slightly thickened.
4. Serve hot or cold with fresh baguette, garnished with fresh parsley or basil.

GRILLED FRESH TUNA WITH ROMESCO SAUCE

Fresh tuna (from line caught sources) is a real treat from our French market. The best way to cook it is to barbecue it. Delicious!

You will need: **Serves 4**

    2 fresh tuna steaks (1 between 2)
    seasoning
    olive oil
    lemon wedges

For the sauce:

    1 slice white bread, diced
    ½ red chilli, diced finely
    2 cloves garlic, peeled and finely chopped
    3 ripe tomatoes, peeled
    100 g (4 oz) toasted, flaked almonds
    ½ jar roasted red peppers
    Juice of 1 lemon
    50 ml (2 fluid oz) olive oil

Method:

1. Make the sauce first, while the barbecue is heating. Fry the bread, chilli and garlic in a pan with a little oil until it begins to colour.
2. Blend with the tomatoes, nuts and peppers and add the lemon juice, seasoning and a little olive oil.
3. Cook the tuna on a hot grill, turning every few minutes. Don't overcook it, but it will take longer than most fish because it is quite dense in texture.
4. Serve with a drizzle of olive oil and the sauce on the side, with lemon wedges.

CHINESE PRAWNS IN GARLIC SAUCE

This sounds like a lot of oil, but you only need to use it for deep frying the prawns. The rest of the food is then cooked in the residual oil left in the pan.

You will need: Serves 3—4

225 g (8 oz) peeled prawns
850 ml (30 fluid oz) vegetable oil
1 teaspoon sesame oil
170 g (6 oz) sugar/mangetout peas
75 g (3 oz) sliced water chestnuts
50 g (2 oz) diced red pepper
25 g (1 oz) mushrooms
1 teaspoon chilli paste
1 teaspoon chopped root ginger
2 teaspoons fresh chopped garlic

For the marinade/coating:

½ teaspoon salt
½ teaspoon egg white
2 tablespoons cornflour
1 tablespoon oil

For the garlic sauce mixture:

1 tablespoon soy sauce
I tablespoon sugar
1 tablespoon lemon juice
1 tablespoon white wine
I tablespoon seafood stock or water
1½ teaspoons cornflour

Method:
1. Wash and dry the prawns. Mix the ingredients for the marinade together, add the prawns and leave for about 2 hours in a refrigerator.
2. Meanwhile mix the garlic sauce ingredients together and leave to one side.
3. Heat a wok or frying pan over a high heat for at least 20 seconds and then add the oil.
4. Add the marinated prawns to the wok and cook for about 30 seconds, then remove the prawns and drain well. Pour the oil out into a bowl to cool.

5. Keep the residual oil in the wok, then add the chilli, ginger and garlic. Cook for 10 seconds. Add the garlic sauce mixture and cook until it thickens.

6. Add the rest of the vegetables and cook for about 20 seconds over a high heat, until just cooked. Return the prawns to the wok and stir all ingredients thoroughly. Serve immediately.

ROLLMOPS

You will need: **Serves 4—6**

    6 fresh herrings
    1 tablespoon salt
    1 teaspoon black pepper
    3 small onions, chopped
    25 g (1 oz) sugar
    3 bay leaves
    2 tablespoons water
    285 ml (10 fluid oz) white wine vinegar
    Pinch of allspice

Method:

1. Cut the herrings into fillets and place them in a large pan.

2. Scatter salt and pepper, allspice and onions over them. Pour over the liquids and add the bay leaves and sugar.

3. Bring to the boil for 2 minutes and then remove from the heat and leave to cool in the pan until ready to serve.

ROASTED PEPPERS WITH GARLIC AND ANCHOVIES

This is a simple hors d'oeuvres, or good side dish for barbecues. You can leave out the anchovies and go for chopped fresh herbs, such as thyme, or spices, such as crushed cumin or fennel seeds. The peppers can be prepared in advance and left covered until you want them.

You will need: Serves 4

- 1 kg (2 lb) sweet peppers, preferably not green
- 2 tablespoons olive oil
- 1 small tin anchovies, drained
- 2 garlic cloves, sliced
- ⅛ teaspoon salt
- Black pepper
- 2 tablespoons chopped fresh basil

Method:
1. Preheat the oven to 220°C (425°F, gas mark 7).
2. Halve and quarter each pepper lengthwise, and remove the seeds and the white membranes.
3. Brush each pepper section with olive oil, and arrange, skin side down, on a baking sheet.
4. Slice the anchovies in half. Place one half and 2 slices of garlic in the cavity of each pepper quarter. Brush these with the remaining oil. Sprinkle lightly with salt and generously with pepper.
5. Roast for about 20–25 minutes, until the peppers are collapsed, tender, and slightly browned on the edges.
6. Sprinkle the basil over the peppers just before serving. These can be eaten hot or at room temperature.

ROAST SALMON WITH BALSAMIC GLAZE

This is a very special way of preparing baked salmon, and will serve 8 to 10 people. It is good served hot or cold.

You will need:
- 2 kg (4 lb) whole salmon
- 1 tablespoon grated lemon rind
- 2 cloves crushed garlic
- 1 small onion
- 2 tablespoons chopped fresh thyme
- 3 tablespoons olive oil
- 6 tablespoons balsamic vinegar
- 1 teaspoon granulated sugar
- 6 tablespoons red wine
- 1 lemon (for garnish)

Method:
1. Chop together the lemon rind, garlic, onion and thyme.
2. Brush oil over the salmon and inside the cavity. Rub the herb mixture all over.
3. Preheat the oven to 180°C (350°F, gas mark 4). Place the salmon in a baking dish lined with foil and roast for 40 minutes or until the juices run clear. Leave it to rest for about 15 minutes after removing from the oven.
4. Meanwhile combine the balsamic vinegar, wine and sugar in a saucepan. Bring to the boil and reduce the liquid until it is syrupy.
5. Before serving, remove the skin from the fish and add any juices to the sauce. Skim off excess fat and pour the sauce over the fish. Serve garnished with lemon wedges.

SARDINES IN ONION, GARLIC AND TOMATO

If you haven't had fresh sardines, they are worth a go. They are so much nicer than tinned ones and taste great barbecued. If you want to skin the tomatoes, sit them in a bowl of very hot water for a few minutes to burst the skins. Remove from the water and the skins will fall off.

You will need: Serves 4
    450 g (1 lb) fresh sardines
    2 tablespoons oil
    1 medium onion, chopped
    2 cloves garlic, crushed
    450 g (1 lb) fresh, ripe tomatoes
    2 tablespoons tomato purée
    Salt and pepper
    1 tablespoon fresh basil, chopped

Method:
1. Clean the fish by removing the entrails and wash thoroughly under running water.
2. Place the fish on a grill and cook for about 8–10 minutes, turning once.
3. Meanwhile, make the sauce by heating the oil in a pan. Add the onion and garlic.
4. Chop the tomatoes and add them to the pan with the purée. Simmer to thicken. Stir in the basil and season with salt and pepper.
5. Serve with fresh bread and the sauce on the side.

Ornamental
Alliums

The following is a list of some other alliums, grown for their flowers rather than for eating.

ALLIUM AFLATUNENSE
This is a plant from Central Asia that grows to over a metre in height. Strap-shaped grey-green leaves can be 10 centimetres (4 inches) across and the star-shaped flowers produced in late spring are pinkish and good for cutting. 'Purple Sensation' is a form with large spheres of blossom in, as you might expect, dark purple.

ALLIUM ALBOPILOSUM
From the Middle East, this has strap-shaped leaves which are grey and hairy underneath. The large heads of up to 80 flowers are a metallic lilac. It flowers in June and then you have the added bonus of spectacular seed heads.

ALLIUM AZUREUM
From Siberia, the leaves are linear. It produces deep blue star-shaped flowers in umbels in June and July.

ALLIUM BABINGTONII
This is now a rare plant, found in rocky and sandy places in the south-west of England and in western Ireland.
It was once collected and eaten, but now it is grown for the large, loose round flower heads which are mixtures of deep purple flowers and bulbils. It can be cultivated from bulbils, obviously from suppliers of seeds, rather than from the wild.

ALLIUM BEESIANUM
This comes from China. Bright blue or purple bell-shaped flowers bloom between July and August. The leek-like stem replaces a bulb.

ALLIUM BULGARICUM
Good for dried flower lovers. Large, bell-shaped cream/green flowers have a flush of purple. They have the most unusual habit of drooping from the top of the stems until pollinated, when they stand up, straight and erect. Nice.

ALLIUM CAERULEUM
See *A. azureum*.

ALLIUM CANADENSE
Although this is an ornamental you can dig it up and eat it when young. The umbels are white to pink, and can be all bulbils, all flowers or a mixture. Good value really.

ALLIUM CERNUUM
This one comes from the USA. Very narrow leaves and loose umbels of nodding pink/purple flowers appear in early summer.

ALLIUM GIGANTEUM
From the Himalayas, this plant lives up to its name, growing to 130 centimetres (4 feet). The leaves are strap-shaped and green/blue. Huge flowers 10 centimetres (4 inches) wide appear in June in a deep lilac colour.

ALLIUM LENKORANICUM
This plant was discovered in the 1980s in Azerbaijan near the Caspian Sea at 2,000 metres (6,000 feet) above sea level. It has long, very thin leaves. The flowers are cream to lilac/rose bells, with each petal bearing a maroon or purple stripe. It grows to about 45 centimetres (18 inches).

ALLIUM MOLY
From southern Europe, the bright yellow flowers appear in June and July and the leaves are a greyish green.

ALLIUM NARCISSIFLORUM
Coming from the French Alps, it has linear grey-green leaves and deep, bell-shaped, bright pink flowers. Like the *A. Bulgaricum*, it starts drooping but then stands up straight. Coming from limestone country, it is a small plant 15—30 centimetres (6—12 inches).

ALLIUM NEAPOLITANUM
From the Mediterranean, this plant is only hardy in milder areas. Mid-green leaves and white flowers from March to May.

ALLIUM OREOPHILUM
From Turkestan, this plant has glaucous, drooping leaves and star-shaped, rose-coloured flowers in June.

ALLIUM ROSENBACHIANUM
The spiky leaves are mid-green. Huge flowers, tightly packed in umbels of over 10 centimetres (4 inches) are rich purple/violet. Good for cut flowers, this plant grows to 1 metre (3 feet).

ALLIUM ROSEUM
From the western Mediterranean, it grows to a height of 30 centimetres (12 inches) and has large pink, star-shaped flowers in June and linear foliage.

ALLIUM SPHAEROCEPHALON
This round-headed leek is found throughout Europe and is easy to grow. It has dense heads of reddish purple flowers in summer.

ALLIUM SCHUBERTII
From the eastern Mediterranean, this allium grows to 60 centimetres (2 feet). Huge umbels 10—15 centimetres (4—6 inches) wide flower in a rose-red colour in summer.

ALLIUM THUNBERGII 'OZAWA'
Known in the USA as the Fall Onion, it blooms in the autumn, producing rose/purple flowers in September and October. The leaves can be eaten and turn a bronze colour when the weather cools. Good value.

ALLIUM URSINUM
This native flower is called Ramsons Wood Garlic. It flowers (and smells) in damp, shady places. In spring it has pretty white, star-shaped flowers. Good for ground cover.

ALLIUM ZEBDANENSE
This comes from the Lebanon and Turkey. It produces only a few leaves and a few bell-shaped white flowers in May.